OXFORD

Maths Links

9A

Claire Turpin

Contents

D1630886

Homework Book

Great Clarendon Street, Oxford OX2 6DP

Oxford University Press is a department of the University of Oxford.
It furthers the University's objective of excellence in research, scholarship,
and education by publishing worldwide in

Oxford   New York

Auckland   Cape Town   Dar es Salaam   Hong Kong   Karachi
Kuala Lumpur   Madrid   Melbourne   Mexico City   Nairobi
New Delhi   Shanghai   Taipei   Toronto

With offices in

Argentina   Austria   Brazil   Chile   Czech Republic   France   Greece
Guatemala   Hungary   Italy   Japan   South Korea   Poland   Portugal
Singapore   Switzerland   Thailand   Turkey   Ukraine   Vietnam

Oxford is a registered trade mark of Oxford University Press
in the UK and in certain other countries

British Library Cataloguing in Publication Data

Data available

ISBN 9780199153107

10 9 8 7 6 5 4

Printed in Great Britain by Ashford Colour Press Ltd, Gosport

Paper used in the production of this book is a natural, recyclable product
made from wood grown in sustainable forests. The manufacturing process
conforms to the environmental regulations of the country of origin.

example

Complete the missing numbers in this sequence
12, ..., 30, 39, ..., 57 and give the term-to-term rule.
....

The term-to-term rule is 'add 9', so the sequence is
12, 21, 30, 39, 48, 57.

1 For each pattern
  i write the sequence   **ii** write the term-to-term rule.
  a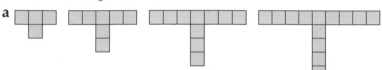

  b

2 For each sequence
  i write the term-to-term rule
  ii use the rule to find the next three terms of the sequence.
  a 6, 10, 14, 18, ...   **b** 3, 8, 13, 18, ...   **c** 21, 17, 13, 9, ...
  d 125, 250, 375, 500, ...   **e** 1.5, 3, 4.5, 6, ...   **f** 15, 10, 5, 0, ...

3 James saves his £6 pocket money each week in his piggy bank.
  He has £20 already.
  a Copy and complete this sequence for the money he is saving
    each week.
    20, ..., ..., ..., ..., ..., ..., ...
  b What is the term-to-term rule for the amount of money in
    James's piggy bank?

4 Copy and complete these sequences by filling in the missing
  numbers. Give the term-to-term rule for each one.
  a 15, ..., 35, 45, ..., ..., 75   **b** 12, ..., 8, 6, ..., ..., 0
  c 88, 76, ..., 52, ..., ..., 16   **d** 5, 3, ..., -1, ..., ..., -7
  e ..., 25, 10, ..., ..., -35, ...   **f** 0.25, ..., ..., 1, 1.25, ...

1 Here are two flow charts. Follow the instructions to generate a sequence from each flow chart. The first one has been done as an example.

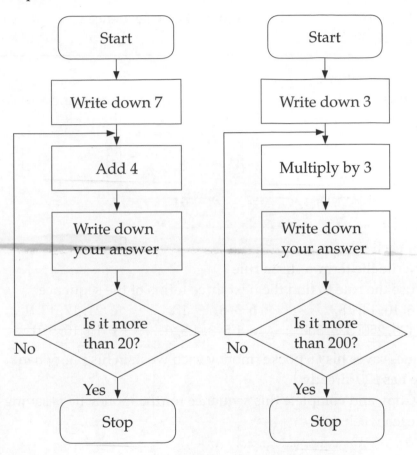

The sequence is 7, 11, 15, 19, 23.

2 Draw a flow chart to generate each of the following sequences.

a 6, 10, 14, 18, 22   **b** 0.5, 0.75, 1, 1.25, 1.5, 1.75, 2

c 16, 8, 4, 2, 1, 0.5   **d** 1, -2, 4, -8, 16, -32

e 12, 6, 0, -6, -12, -18   **f** 0.2, 0.4, 0.8, 1.6, 3.2, 6.4

For the sequence 4, 7, 10, 13, 16, work out the position-to-term rule.

· ·

4,   7,   10,   13,   16
  +3   +3   +3   +3

3   6   9   12   15
  +1   +1   +1   +1
4   7   10   13   16

The rule is $3n + 1$

Because the sequence goes up in threes, it is based on the three times table. You can see that, to make the sequence, you need to add one onto the three times tables.

1 For each mapping

  i copy and complete each pattern

  ii write the rule which connects the position of the term to the value of the term

  iii use your rule to work out the 10th term, the 50th term and the 100th term.

a Position	Term	b Position	Term	c Position	Term
1 →	5	1 →	10	1 →	8
2 →	9	2 →	13	2 →	15
3 →	13	3 →	16	3 →	22
4 →		4 →		4 →	
5 →		5 →		5 →	

d Position	Term	e Position	Term	f Position	Term
1 →	25	1 →	4	1 →	3
2 →	35	2 →	10	2 →	7
3 →	45	3 →	16	3 →	11
4 →		4 →		4 →	
5 →		5 →		5 →	

2 For each of these sequences work out the position-to-term rule. You can use mapping to help.

  a 6, 10, 14, 18, 22, ...   **b** 15, 18, 21, 24, 27, 30, ...

  c 1, 5, 9, 13, 17, ...   **d** 3.5, 5.5, 7.5, 9.5, ...

1d Functions

example

Copy and complete this function machine:

Input		Output
1	→×2→	2
2		4
3		☐
4		☐

Input		Output
1	→×2→	2
2		4
3		6
4		8

1 Copy and complete each of these function machines

a
Input		Output
1		☐
2	→÷2→	☐
3		☐
4		☐

b
Input		Output
1		☐
2	→×12→	☐
3		☐
4		☐

2 Gabriel is saving money. Every time he helps his dad in the kitchen he gets 50p.

a Copy and complete the function machine to calculate how much money he earns as he helps in the kitchen. Give your answers in pounds.

Input		Output
1		☐
2	→☐→	☐
3		☐
4		☐

b Use the function machine to calculate the amount of money Gabriel earns, in pounds, when he helps out in the kitchen

i 5 times   **ii** 6 times   **iii** 11 times   **iv** 13 times.

1e Mappings

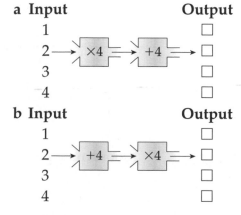

example

Copy and complete this two-step function machine:

Input		Output
1		5
2 →×2 →+3 →		7
3		☐
4		☐

Input		Output
1		5
2 →×2 →+3 →		7
3		9
4		11

1 Copy and complete these two-step function machines.

a
Input		Output
1		☐
2 →×4 →+4 →		☐
3		☐
4		☐

b
Input		Output
1		☐
2 →+4 →×4 →		☐
3		☐
4		☐

2 Stephen goes to the fair. He has to pay a £3.50 entrance fee and 50p per ride. The total cost is a function of the number of rides he goes on.

a Copy and complete the cost of going on the rides.

Number of rides		Total cost
1	→	☐
4	→	☐
7	→	☐
10	→	☐
13	→	☐

b How many rides could he go on if he had £15?

1f Graphs of functions

1 a Complete the function machine and write the values for the mapping as coordinate pairs.

Input		Output	Coordinate pairs
x		y	
1		☐	(,)
2		☐	(,)
3		☐	(,)
4		☐	(,)

b Copy the grid onto square paper and plot these points.

c Join the points to make a straight line.

d Use your graph to work out the value of the fifth pattern.

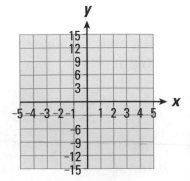

2 a Complete the function machine and write the values for the mapping as coordinate pairs.

Input		Output	Coordinate pairs
x		y	
1		☐	(,)
2	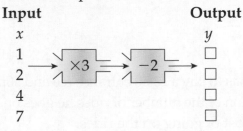	☐	(,)
4		☐	(,)
7		☐	(,)

b Copy the grid onto square paper and plot the points.

c Join the points to make a straight line.

d Use your graph to work out the value of the eighth pattern.

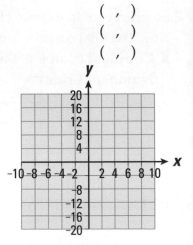

example

Work out these fractions.

a $\dfrac{4}{7} + \dfrac{2}{7}$　　　　b $\dfrac{8}{9} - \dfrac{4}{9}$　　　　c $\dfrac{7}{10} - \dfrac{2}{10}$

. . . .

a $\dfrac{4}{7} + \dfrac{2}{7} = \dfrac{4+2}{7} = \dfrac{6}{7}$　　　　b $\dfrac{8}{9} - \dfrac{4}{9} = \dfrac{8-4}{9} = \dfrac{4}{9}$

c $\dfrac{7}{10} - \dfrac{2}{10} = \dfrac{7-2}{10} = \dfrac{5}{10} = \dfrac{1}{2}$

1 Laura's birthday cake is cut into ten equal pieces.

  a What fraction is each piece?

  Laura eats $\dfrac{1}{10}$ of the cake. Jade eats $\dfrac{2}{10}$ of the cake.

  b What fraction of the cake do they eat altogether?

  c What fraction of the cake is left?

2 Add these fractions.

  a $\dfrac{1}{5} + \dfrac{2}{5}$　　　　**b** $\dfrac{2}{7} + \dfrac{3}{7}$　　　　**c** $\dfrac{1}{8} + \dfrac{1}{8} + \dfrac{3}{8}$

  d $\dfrac{4}{6} + \dfrac{1}{6}$　　　　**e** $\dfrac{3}{10} + \dfrac{1}{10} + \dfrac{1}{10}$　　　　**f** $\dfrac{6}{11} + \dfrac{1}{11} + \dfrac{4}{11}$

3 Subtract these fractions.

  a $\dfrac{6}{7} - \dfrac{2}{7}$　　　　**b** $\dfrac{4}{9} - \dfrac{1}{9}$　　　　**c** $\dfrac{7}{9} - \dfrac{2}{9}$

  d $\dfrac{9}{11} - \dfrac{2}{11}$　　　　**e** $\dfrac{10}{13} - \dfrac{2}{13} - \dfrac{5}{13}$　　　　**f** $\dfrac{3}{7} - \dfrac{2}{7} - \dfrac{1}{7}$

4 Are these statements true or false?

  a $\dfrac{10}{10}$ is the same as 1.　　　　**b** $\dfrac{4}{5}$ is less than $\dfrac{1}{2}$.

  c $\dfrac{2}{5}$ plus $\dfrac{4}{5}$ is more than 1.　　　　**d** $\dfrac{8}{9}$ take away $\dfrac{2}{9}$ is the same as $\dfrac{2}{3}$.

5 Replace the empty boxes with $+$ and $-$ signs to make these statements correct.

  a $\dfrac{1}{3} \square \dfrac{1}{3} \square \dfrac{1}{3} = 1$　　　　**b** $\dfrac{4}{5} \square \dfrac{1}{5} \square \dfrac{2}{5} = \dfrac{1}{5}$

  c $\dfrac{7}{9} \square \dfrac{1}{9} \square \dfrac{4}{9} = \dfrac{4}{9}$　　　　**d** $\dfrac{5}{12} \square \dfrac{4}{12} \square \dfrac{3}{12} = \dfrac{1}{2}$

example

Work out   **a** $\frac{2}{3}+\frac{1}{9}$ **b** $\frac{7}{12}-\frac{1}{2}$

a $\frac{2}{3}=\frac{6}{9}$ so $\frac{2}{3}+\frac{1}{9}=\frac{6}{9}+\frac{1}{9}=\frac{7}{9}$

b $\frac{1}{2}=\frac{6}{12}$ so $\frac{7}{12}-\frac{1}{2}=\frac{7}{12}-\frac{6}{12}=\frac{1}{12}$

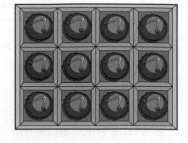

1 Manjit and Shane share a box of chocolates.

Manjit eats $\frac{1}{3}$ of the chocolates and Shane eats $\frac{1}{4}$.

   a Use the picture to calculate the total fraction of the box that they have eaten.

   b What fraction of the box of chocolates is left?

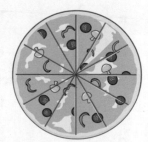

2 The diagram shows a pizza divided into 12 equal pieces.

Use the diagram to help you add and subtract these fractions.

   a $\frac{3}{12}+\frac{1}{12}$ **b** $\frac{5}{6}-\frac{3}{12}$ **c** $\frac{11}{12}-\frac{5}{6}$

   d $\frac{1}{4}+\frac{2}{6}$ **e** $\frac{5}{6}-\frac{1}{12}$ **f** $\frac{1}{4}+\frac{1}{6}$

3 Chloe and Rhiannon went to the fair.

Chloe went on $\frac{2}{15}$ of the rides.

Rhiannon went on $\frac{11}{30}$ of the rides.

They didn't go on the same rides.

   a What fraction of the rides did they go on?

   b What fraction of the rides did neither of them go on?

Calculate these.   **a** $\frac{1}{3}$ of 27 g   **b** $\frac{5}{7}$ of £56

· ·

a To calculate $\frac{1}{3}$ of a number you divide by three.

$$27 \longrightarrow \boxed{\div 3} \longrightarrow 9$$

b To find $\frac{5}{7}$ of £56 first find $\frac{1}{7}$:

£56 ÷ 7 = £8, then multiply the result by 5: £8 × 5 = £40 or use a function machine.

$$£56 \longrightarrow \boxed{\div 7} £8 \boxed{\times 5} \longrightarrow £40$$

1 Calculate these.

a $\frac{1}{4}$ of £24   **b** $\frac{1}{6}$ of 36 g   **c** $\frac{1}{9}$ of 63 cm

d $\frac{1}{7}$ of 21p   **e** $\frac{1}{10}$ of 110 m   **f** $\frac{1}{5}$ of £85

g $\frac{1}{2}$ of £35   **h** $\frac{1}{3}$ of 240 mm   **i** $\frac{1}{12}$ of 96 kg

j $\frac{1}{5}$ of £200   **k** $\frac{1}{15}$ of 60 tonnes   **l** $\frac{1}{8}$ of 128 euros

2 Use two operations to calculate these.

a $\frac{2}{3}$ of 12 kg   **b** $\frac{3}{7}$ of £35   **c** $\frac{4}{5}$ of $45

d $\frac{5}{6}$ of 120 cm   **e** $\frac{4}{10}$ of 1000 m   **f** $\frac{7}{8}$ of 64 volts

g $\frac{4}{9}$ of 72 g   **h** $\frac{2}{7}$ of 49 pupils   **i** $\frac{11}{20}$ of 200 mm

j $\frac{3}{7}$ of 63 kg   **k** $\frac{6}{13}$ of 52 cards   **l** $\frac{21}{25}$ of £500

3 In an athletics competition, Harborne Harriers won 36 medals: 2 were Gold, 20 were Silver and the rest were Bronze.

  a What fraction of the medals were Bronze?

  b $\frac{3}{7}$ of the Bronze medals were won by the male athletes. How many Bronze medals were won by the male athletes?

4 Ninety pupils go on a school trip to France, $\frac{7}{15}$ are girls.

  a How many are girls?

  b Of the remaining boys, $\frac{3}{8}$ of them are in Year 7. How many Year 7 boys are there?

2d Multiplying and dividing fractions

Work these out. **a** $\frac{1}{3} \times 12$ **b** $3 \div \frac{1}{4}$

a $\frac{1}{3} \times 12 = 4$

1 whole   1 whole   1 whole   1 whole

b $3 \div \frac{1}{4} = 3 \times \frac{4}{1} = 12$

There are 12 quarters in three wholes.

1 Work these out.

a $\frac{1}{2} \times 40$ **b** $\frac{1}{3} \times 18$ **c** $\frac{1}{4} \times 20$ **d** $\frac{1}{5} \times 25$

e $\frac{1}{7} \times 49$ **f** $\frac{1}{8} \times 40$ **g** $\frac{1}{10} \times 80$ **h** $\frac{1}{9} \times 63$

i $\frac{1}{20} \times 100$ **j** $\frac{1}{6} \times 48$ **k** $45 \times \frac{1}{9}$ **l** $55 \times \frac{1}{11}$

2 Divide these whole numbers by fractions.

a $5 \div \frac{1}{4}$ **b** $6 \div \frac{1}{3}$ **c** $9 \div \frac{1}{2}$ **d** $2 \div \frac{1}{5}$

e $4 \div \frac{1}{4}$ **f** $20 \div \frac{1}{3}$ **g** $15 \div \frac{1}{6}$ **h** $30 \div \frac{1}{7}$

i $14 \div \frac{1}{8}$ **j** $100 \div \frac{1}{3}$ **k** $30 \div \frac{1}{9}$ **l** $25 \div \frac{1}{12}$

3 Sonia cuts four pizzas into eighths.

  a Which of these calculations is the correct one to work out the total number of pieces: $4 \div \frac{1}{8}$ or $4 \times \frac{1}{8}$?

  b How many pieces are there in total?

4 A teacher marks a class set of books. She decides to spend $\frac{1}{10}$ of an hour on each book.

  a Which of these calculations is the correct one to work out the total number of books she can mark in 3 hours: $3 \div \frac{1}{10}$ or $3 \times \frac{1}{10}$?

  b How many books can she mark in the 3 hours?

example

Convert these fractions to decimals.

a $\frac{4}{10}$ **b** $\frac{4}{5}$ **c** $\frac{3}{8}$ **d** $\frac{4}{9}$

. . . .

a We know that $\frac{1}{10}$ is 0.1, so $\frac{4}{10} = 4 \times 0.1 = 0.4$

b We know $\frac{1}{5} = \frac{2}{10} = 0.2$, so $\frac{4}{5} = 0.2 \times 4 = 0.8$

c For harder fractions you can use a calculator to do the division, i.e. $\frac{3}{8}$ means $3 \div 8 = 0.375$

d Some fractions have recurring decimals, e.g.
$\frac{4}{9} = 4 \div 9 = 0.444444.. \approx 0.44$ to 2 decimal places

1 Convert these fractions to decimals without using a calculator.

a $\frac{6}{10}$ **b** $\frac{1}{5}$ **c** $\frac{2}{5}$ **d** $\frac{3}{10}$

e $\frac{1}{4}$ **f** $\frac{9}{10}$ **g** $\frac{3}{4}$ **h** $\frac{10}{10}$

2 Which of these numbers is the biggest? Use a < or > sign. If they are the same size use the = sign.

a 0.4 or $\frac{1}{2}$ **b** $\frac{1}{10}$ or 0.8 **c** 0.4 or $\frac{1}{5}$

d $\frac{3}{10}$ or 0.3 **e** $\frac{2}{5}$ or 0.3 **f** 0.4 or $\frac{1}{5}$

g $\frac{6}{10}$ or 0.7 **h** $\frac{1}{2}$ or $\frac{2}{5}$ **i** $\frac{7}{10}$ or $\frac{3}{4}$

3 Use a calculator to convert these fractions into decimals. Round the numbers to 2 decimal places when the decimal is recurring.

a $\frac{1}{3}$ **b** $\frac{6}{20}$ **c** $\frac{7}{8}$ **d** $\frac{9}{20}$ **e** $\frac{1}{12}$ **f** $\frac{7}{9}$

4 Convert these fractions into decimals. Then use < or > sign to show which one is biggest. If they are the same size use the = sign.

a $\frac{4}{9}$ or $\frac{1}{4}$ **b** $\frac{3}{20}$ or $\frac{3}{8}$ **c** $\frac{1}{9}$ or $\frac{1}{8}$

d $\frac{4}{6}$ or $\frac{6}{9}$ **e** $\frac{1}{3}$ or $\frac{1}{6}$ **f** $\frac{5}{12}$ or $\frac{7}{9}$

g $\frac{5}{8}$ or $\frac{4}{9}$ **h** $\frac{5}{11}$ or $\frac{3}{8}$ **i** $\frac{2}{7}$ or $\frac{3}{20}$

> **example**
>
> Work out: **a** 30% of 40 kg   **b** 34% of £42
>
> ・・・
>
> **a** First work out 10% of 40 kg by dividing 40 kg by 10.
> Now multiply by 3 to get 30%,
> i.e. 30% of 40 kg = 40 kg ÷ 10 × 3 = 12 kg
>
> **b** 34% means $\frac{34}{100}$ so use a calculator.
> 34 ÷ 100 × £42 = £14.28

1 Work out these percentages of quantities without using a calculator.

a 10% of £40	**b** 10% of 90 kg	**c** 10% of 30 g
d 10% of 55 cm	**e** 10% of $32	**f** 10% of 85 euros
g 10% of 200°	**h** 10% of 45 tonnes	**i** 10% of £95

2 Work out these percentages of quantities without using a calculator.

a 20% of £60	**b** 40% of £30	**c** 80% of 50 kg
d 40% of 80 cm	**e** 60% of 400 mm	**f** 30% of 55 litres
g 90% of 120 euros	**h** 80% of $90	**i** 70% of 130 mm

3 Write these percentages as fractions with a denominator of 100.

a 53%	**b** 97%	**c** 7%
d 29%	**e** 11%	**f** 1%
g 36%	**h** 49%	**i** 5%

4 Calculate these percentages of quantities.

a 13% of 40 kg	**b** 15% of £65	**c** 24% of 125 cm
d 19% of 90 litres	**e** 39% of 12 m	**f** 93% of 360°
g 48% of 250 euros	**h** 67% of 125 ml	**i** 3% of £3000

2g Percentages and proportion

example

Mohammed scored 34 out of 100 in his maths test.
a Write this score as a percentage.
He scored 21 out of 25 in his English test.
b Which test did he do better in?

. . . .

a $\frac{34}{100} = 34\%$

b $\frac{21}{25} = \frac{84}{100} = 84\%$, so he did better in the English test.

1 Write these fractions as percentages.

a $\frac{24}{100}$ **b** $\frac{85}{100}$ **c** $\frac{45}{100}$

d $\frac{12}{100}$ **e** $\frac{4}{100}$ **f** $\frac{97}{100}$

g $\frac{16}{100}$ **h** $\frac{34}{100}$ **i** $\frac{2}{100}$

2 Copy and complete these pairs of equivalent fractions.

a $\frac{2}{10} = \frac{\square}{100}$ **b** $\frac{3}{5} = \frac{\square}{100}$ **c** $\frac{1}{4} = \frac{\square}{100}$

d $\frac{9}{10} = \frac{\square}{100}$ **e** $\frac{14}{25} = \frac{\square}{100}$ **f** $\frac{19}{20} = \frac{\square}{100}$

g $\frac{26}{50} = \frac{\square}{100}$ **h** $\frac{4}{25} = \frac{\square}{100}$ **i** $\frac{7}{20} = \frac{\square}{100}$

3 In a Geography survey Kylie did for her coursework, she found
that 21 out of 25 adults surveyed did their weekly shopping at an
out-of-town supermarket, rather than at a local grocer's shop.
a What fraction did their weekly shopping at a supermarket?
b Convert the fraction to an equivalent fraction with a
denominator of 100.
c What percentage of adults surveyed did their shopping at:
  i the supermarket?
  ii the local grocer's shop?

4 Sandra scored 31 out of 50 in her French test and 14 out of 20 in
her Spanish test.
In which test did she do better?

Simplify each of these ratios as much as possible.

a 4:20   **b** 20:36

a 4:20
2:10 ⎫ ÷ 2
1:5 ⎬ ÷ 2

b 20:36
10:18 ⎫ ÷ 2
5:9 ⎬ ÷ 2

1 a Complete the equivalent ratios on the spider diagram.

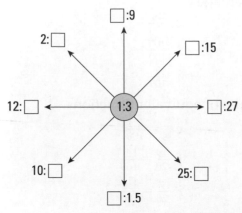

b Add five of your own equivalent ratios.

2 Simplify each of these ratios as much as possible.

a 4:10	**b** 12:20	**c** 20:25	**d** 18:12
e 35:21	**f** 15:45	**g** 36:48	**h** 16:24
i 36:144	**j** 20:28	**k** 16: 72	**l** 121:33

3 A scale drawing of a piece of furniture is made. The ratio used is 2:25. If the furniture is 150 cm wide in real life, how wide will the scale drawing be?

Tinky and Honey share 20 dog treats in the ratio 3:1.
How many dog treats do they each get?

. . . .

3:1 ⟶ 4
There are 5 units of 4 dog treats (20 in total).
So multiply the ratio by 5.
$3 \times 5 = 15$ $1 \times 5 = 5$
Tinky gets 15 dog treats and Honey gets 5.

1 By drawing, share the 20 dog treats
in the following ratios.

  a 4:1

  b 2:3

  c 3:7

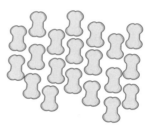

2 a Divide £9 in the ratio 1:2   (Remember 1:2 ⟶ 3)

  b Divide 12kg in the ratio 1:3   (Remember 1:3 ⟶ 4)

  c Divide 25 sweets in the ratio 3:2   (Remember 3:2 ⟶ 5)

  d Divide £36 in the ratio 1:5   (Remember 1:5 ⟶ 6)

  e Divide 50kg in the ratio 7:3   (Remember 7:3 ⟶ 10)

  f Divide 35 apples in the ratio 2:5   (Remember 2:5 ⟶ 7)

  g Divide 72 sweets in the ratio 5:3   (Remember 5:3 ⟶ 8)

  h Divide 56m in the ratio 3:4   (Remember 3:4 ⟶ 7)

3 Sonia and Trevor win £140 in a raffle. They share the money in the
ratio 4:3. Sonia keeps the larger share.
How much will each of them receive?

4 Sanjiv and Alice share 12 chocolates in the ratio 1:3. Sanjiv has the
smaller share. How many chocolates does Alice get?

David is paid £8 an hour. Use the diagram to work out how much he gets paid for 5 hours' work.

Time : wages
1 : 8
5 : □ ⟩ ×5

. . . .

When David works for 5 hours, the multiplier is 5.
(You multiply the ratio by the multiplier.)
When he works for 5 hours David earns £40.

Time : wages
1 : 8
5 : 40 ⟩ ×5

1 Copy these diagrams.
Find the multipliers and complete the diagrams.

a 4:5
16:□ ⟩ ×□

b 2:3
10:□ ⟩ ×□

c 1:4
5:□ ⟩ ×□

d 5:4
15:□ ⟩ ×□

e 1:5
□:25 ⟩ ×□

f 2:3
□:12 ⟩ ×□

2 It takes a builder 20 minutes to build one layer of a wall.
How long would it take to build a wall with 10 layers?

3 Tina can swim 40 metres in one minute.
How many metres will she swim in nine minutes?

4 Juntian can run 200 metres in 24 seconds.
Calculate how long it would take him to run 1000 m.

5 Jade works for four hours and is paid £32.
Work out how much she would be paid for
a 15 hours **b** 24 hours work.

3a Angles and lines

example

Which angles are:

a corresponding

b alternate

c vertically opposite?

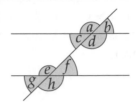

. . . .

a The corresponding angles are: *a* and *e*, *c* and *g*, *b* and *f*, *d* and *h*.

b The alternate angles are: *c* and *f*, *d* and *e*.

c The vertically opposite angles are: *a* and *d*, *c* and *b*, *e* and *h*, *g* and *f*.

1 a Draw a 6 cm line.

  b Draw a line parallel to the first line, 3 cm below it.

  c Draw a line that cuts through both parallel lines, as in the example above.

  d On your diagram, without colouring the same angle twice, colour one pair of:

    i corresponding angles green

    ii alternate angles blue

    iii vertically opposite angles red.

2 a Which is the corresponding angle to angle *s*?

  b Which is the alternate angle to angle *r*?

  c Which is the vertically opposite angle to *t*?

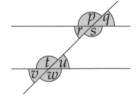

3 In the diagram below, how many angles would you need to measure to be able to work out all of the angles? Explain your answer.

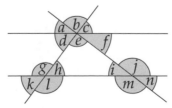

3b Angles in a triangle

a What type of triangle is triangle ABC?
b Find the size of angle ∠ABC.

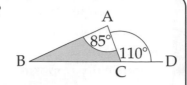

. . . .

a Triangle ABC is a scalene triangle.
b ∠ABC + ∠BAC = ∠ACD, so to work
out ∠ABC, you do 110° − 85° = 25°

> Remember: angles in a
> triangle add up to 180°

1 Draw an example of
  a a scalene triangle   **b** an isosceles triangle
  c an equilateral triangle   **d** a right-angled triangle.

2 The diagram shows the exterior angles of a triangle.
  a Find the size of the interior angles *p*, *q*
    and *r*.
  b Without doing any calculations, state
    what the following will add up to.
    Explain your answers.
    i *p* and *q*   **ii** *p* and *r*   **iii** *q* and *r*

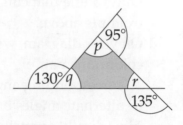

3 Name each of the following triangles and find the size of the angle
  marked *y*. (*Show your working.*)

a

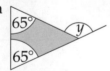

b

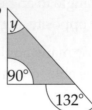

c

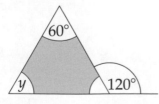

d

3c Properties of triangles

example

Find the size of angle
a ∠ACB
b ∠ACD

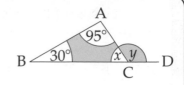

. . . .

a $30° + 95° + x = 180°$

$125° + x = 180°$

$x = 180° - 125° = 55°$

$\angle ACB = 55°$

b $\angle ACD = \angle BAC + \angle ABC$

$\angle ACD = 95° + 30°$

$= 125°$

1 Which of these sets of measurements will not make a triangle?
a 3 cm, 4 cm and 9 cm
b 5 cm, 5 cm and 8 cm
c 12 cm, 14 cm and 10 cm
d 8 cm, 10 cm and 20 cm
e 11 cm, 11 cm and 16 cm

Give an example of a set of measurements that:
i will make a triangle; **ii** will not make a triangle.

2 Find the size of the lettered angles in these triangles.

a
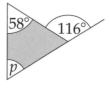

b
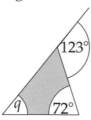

c
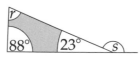

d
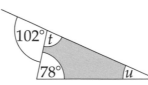

example

Find the size of the missing angle in the quadrilateral

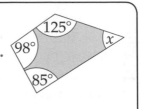

·······································

$125° + 98° + 85° + x = 360°$

$308° + x = 360°$

$x = 360° - 308° = 52°$

1 Find the size of the lettered angles in each of these quadrilaterals.

a

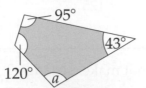

95°
43°
120°
a

b

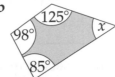

125°
98°
x
85°

c

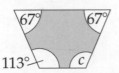

67°   67°
113° c

d

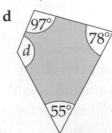

97°
78°
d
55°

e

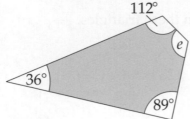

112°
e
36°
89°

f

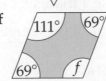

111°   69°
69° f

g

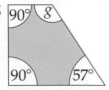

90° g
90°   57°

h

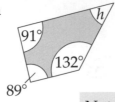

h
91°
132°
89°

2 Which of the shapes above are
   i trapeziums   **ii** parallelograms?

Not all of the shapes have a special name

Match each of the following shapes with their name and properties.

Copy the shape, name and properties into your book, the first one has been matched for you.

Shapes	Names	Properties
	Arrowhead	

Kite

Square

Rhombus

Trapezium

Isosceles Trapezium

Rectangle

Parallelogram

4 equal angles, each 90°
4 equal sides
2 sets of parallel sides

2 sets of equal angles
1 set of equal sides
1 set of parallel sides

Usually has no equal angles
and no equal sides
Always has 1 set of parallel sides

4 equal angles, each 90°
2 sets of equal sides
2 sets of parallel sides

1 pair of equal angles
2 sets of equal sides
No parallel sides

2 pairs of equal angles
2 sets of equal sides
2 sets of parallel sides

2 pairs of equal angles
4 equal sides
2 sets of parallel sides

1 pair of equal angles
2 sets of equal sides
No parallel sides
1 reflex angle

3f Perpendicular bisectors

example

The instructions for how to draw a perpendicular bisector have been jumbled up. Write them out in the correct order.

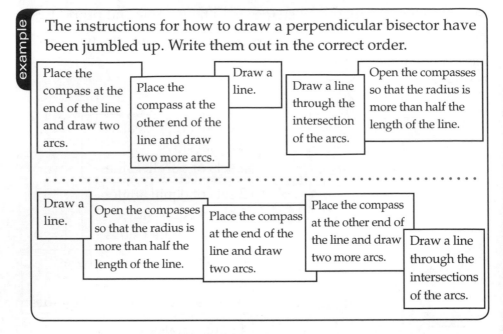

Place the compass at the end of the line and draw two arcs.

Place the compass at the other end of the line and draw two more arcs.

Draw a line.

Draw a line through the intersection of the arcs.

Open the compasses so that the radius is more than half the length of the line.

Draw a line.

Open the compasses so that the radius is more than half the length of the line.

Place the compass at the end of the line and draw two arcs.

Place the compass at the other end of the line and draw two more arcs.

Draw a line through the intersections of the arcs.

1 a Construct a perpendicular bisector for the following length lines:
   i 6 cm   **ii** 11 cm   **iii** 9.5 cm
 b Measure to check that each bisector cuts the line exactly in half.
 c Measure the angles to check that each bisector is at 90° to the line.

2 Draw these lines and construct their perpendicular bisectors.
   i A line 6 cm long at an angle of 40°.
   ii A line 8.5 cm long at an angle of 65°.
   iii A line 7 cm long at an angle of 100°.
   iv A line 10 cm long at an angle of 95°.

3 i Draw an equilateral triangle, of side length 8cm, using a ruler and protractor.
   ii Construct the perpendicular bisectors for each side of the triangle.
   iii What do you notice about where the perpendicular bisectors intersect?

4 Construct a rhombus with side length 6 cm.

3g Angle bisectors

a Draw an acute angle of 60°.

b Bisect the angle using a pair of compasses.

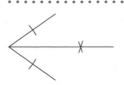

1 Draw these acute angles using a protractor.
Bisect each angle.

a 80°   **b** 50°   **c** 68°

2 Draw these obtuse angles using a protractor.
Bisect each angle.

a 120°   **b** 170°   **c** 136°

3 Draw three different size triangles. Bisect all
of the angles of each triangle. What do you notice?

4 A farmer wants to lay a pipe to run down into the corner of his field.

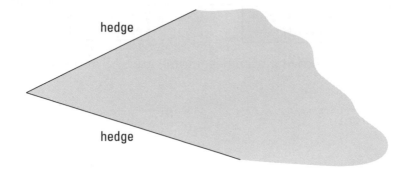

He wants the pipe to be an equal distance from both hedges.
Show where the pipe should be laid.

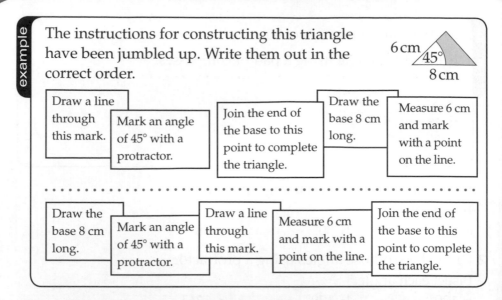

example

The instructions for constructing this triangle have been jumbled up. Write them out in the correct order.

6 cm 45° 8 cm

| Draw a line through this mark. | Mark an angle of 45° with a protractor. | Join the end of the base to this point to complete the triangle. | Draw the base 8 cm long. | Measure 6 cm and mark with a point on the line. |

| Draw the base 8 cm long. | Mark an angle of 45° with a protractor. | Draw a line through this mark. | Measure 6 cm and mark with a point on the line. | Join the end of the base to this point to complete the triangle. |

1 The instructions for constructing this triangle have been jumbled up. Write them out in the correct order.

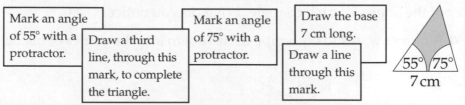

| Mark an angle of 55° with a protractor. | Draw a third line, through this mark, to complete the triangle. | Mark an angle of 75° with a protractor. | Draw the base 7 cm long. Draw a line through this mark. |

55° 75° 7 cm

2 Construct the following triangles – some are SAS and some are ASA.

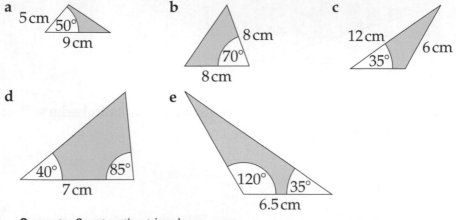

a 5 cm 50° 9 cm

b 8 cm 70° 8 cm

c 12 cm 35° 6 cm

d 40° 85° 7 cm

e 120° 35° 6.5 cm

Jason finds a treasure map.

What is the bearing of the Treasure from the Old House?

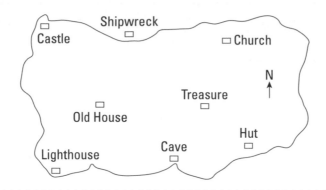

The bearing of the Treasure from the Old House is 090°

1 If Jason is in the Old House what will he see on a bearing of:
   a 020°   **b** 055°   **c** 115°   **d** 215°   **e** 320°?

2 What is the bearing of the Treasure from the:
   a Shipwreck   **b** Castle   **c** Hut   **d** Lighthouse   **e** Cave?

3 Jason finds the treasure and needs to escape. What will he reach if he travels in the following directions:
   a West   **b** North-West   **c** South-East   **d** South-West?

4 Jason travels from the Treasure to the Hut, then to the Lighthouse and finally to the Shipwreck. Give the three bearings that he must use.

Simplify these expressions.

a $g + g + g - g + g$ **b** $3f + 4h - f + 2h$ **c** $3i \times 4j$

. . . .

a $g + g + g - \cancel{g} + \cancel{g}$ **b** $3f - f + 4h + 2h$ **c** $3 \times 4 \times i \times j$

   $= 3g$ $= 2f + 6h$ $= 12ij$

1 Simplify these expressions.

a $m + m + m + m$ **b** $d + d + d + d - d$

c $k + k - k + k - k$ **d** $3s + s + 4s - s$

e $8h - 3h + h - 2h$ **f** $4a + 12a - 4a - a$

g $9x + 3x - 4x + 2x$ **h** $3k + 5k - 8k$

i $3z + 4z - z + 12z$ **j** $13w + 12w - 20w + w - 2w$

2 Simplify these expressions as much as possible.

a $2p + 3p$ **b** $5m - 6n + 2m - 3n$

c $4a + 3b + 3a - 2b$ **d** $3s + 2p - 3s - p$

e $5x + 8y + 2x - 5y - x$ **f** $9w - 4x + w - 3x$

g $3n + 4m - 5m + n + m$ **h** $2a - 2b - 2a + 2b + a$

i $y + 4x - 2y + x$ **j** $4s + 6 + 3s - 4 - s$

3 Simplify these by multiplying and dividing.

a $3 \times 2g$ **b** $4 \times 6h$ **c** $12g \times 4$

d $3 \times 5 \times 3k$ **e** $3p \times 4q$ **f** $6m \times 6n$

g $12w \times 5u$ **h** $3t \times 2a$ **i** $20h \div 4$

j $30h \div 6$ **k** $\dfrac{45f}{5}$ **l** $\dfrac{24j}{4j}$

m $\dfrac{120y}{12y}$ **n** $\dfrac{88j}{11}$ **o** $\dfrac{45p}{15}$

4 Write an expression for the perimeter of each of these shapes.

a

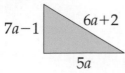

b

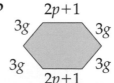

example

Are these statements true or false?

a $20 = 5 \times 5$ **b** $3 \times 4 > 3 + 4$ **c** $120 \div 10 < 10 \times 2$

. . . .

a $5 \times 5 = 25$ **b** $3 \times 4 = 12$ and   **c** $120 \div 10 = 12$ and
$3 + 4 = 7$ $10 \times 2 = 20$

so false   so $12 > 7$ so $12 < 20$
therefore true.   therefore true.

1 Do these pairs of calculations make equations?
Use $=$ for an equation and $\neq$ for not an equation.
a $15 \div 5$ and $9 \div 3$ **b** $20 - 15$ and 2×3
c $36 \div 6$ and $9 - 3$ **d** $12 + 18$ and 5×6
e $55 \div 11$ and 2×3 **f** 16×2 and $64 \div 2$
g $120 - 20$ and $1000 \div 10$ **h** $48 - 12$ and $48 \div 12$
i $240 - 90$ and 15×10 **j** $108 \div 9$ and 12×4

2 Are these statements true or false?
a $20 = 4 \times 5$ **b** $25 < 2 \times 12$ **c** $20 \times 3 > 20 + 20$
d $36 \div 6 = 30 - 6$ **e** $120 - 100 < 20 \times 4$ **f** $5 \times 6 = 15 \times 2$
g $80 \times 3 > 240 \div 4$ **h** $48 \div 12 < 26 \div 2$ **i** $15 \times 5 > 10 \times 10$
j $6 \times 7 > 4 \times 8$ **k** $20 \times 20 = 200 + 200$ **l** $12 \times 12 > 140 - 10$

3 Copy these statements and fill in the missing number to make the
statement true.
a $20 + 2 = 10 + \square$ **b** $16 - 4 = 2 \times \square$ **c** $30 \div 6 = 2 + \square$
d $36 - 6 = 16 + \square$ **e** $40 \div 10 = 55 - \square$ **f** $36 + 4 = 4 \times \square$
g $66 + 4 = 140 \div \square$ **h** $120 \div 20 = 36 \div \square$ **i** $37 + 11 = 12 \times \square$
j $240 \div 48 = 25 - \square$ **k** $52 \div 13 = 4 \times \square$ **l** $65 - 15 = 50 + \square$

Solve these equations.

a $g + 12 = 20$ **b** $3 \times t = 12$ **c** $\dfrac{d}{2} = 5$

. . . .

a $g + 12 = 20$

$g + 12 - 12 = 20 - 12$

$g = 8$

b $3 \times t = 12$

$t \times 3 = 12$

$t \times 3 \div 3 = 12 \div 3$

$t = 4$

c $\dfrac{d}{2} = 5$

$\dfrac{d}{2} \times 2 = 5 \times 2$

$d = 10$

1 Use inverse operations to find the value of each unknown.

a $d \longrightarrow \boxed{\times 3} \longrightarrow 15$

b $g \longrightarrow \boxed{+3} \longrightarrow 19$

c $f \longrightarrow \boxed{\div 3} \longrightarrow 21$

d $h \longrightarrow \boxed{-3} \longrightarrow 6$

2 Solve these equations.

a $t + 5 = 15$ **b** $r - 4 = 10$ **c** $f + 12 = 20$

d $g + 21 = 45$ **e** $v + 23 = 50$ **f** $p - 3 = 33$

3 Solve these equations.

a $10 + y = 20$ **b** $16 + d = 21$ **c** $f - 14 = 2$

d $16 + u = 23$ **e** $q - 15 = 19$ **f** $k - 3 = 3$

4 Find the value of the unknown in each of these equations.

a $4 \times h = 12$ **b** $12 \times t = 48$ **c** $4 \times d = 16$

d $6c = 30$ **e** $7g = 42$ **f** $6b = 48$

5 Find the value of the unknown in each of these equations.

a $d \div 3 = 2$ **b** $t \div 4 = 5$ **c** $q \div 5 = 25$

d $\dfrac{f}{3} = 7$ **e** $\dfrac{h}{6} = 3$ **f** $\dfrac{j}{7} = 7$

4d Balancing equations 1

Solve these equations.

a $p + 15 = 45$ **b** $3y = 36$ **c** $4p + 3 = 27$

. . . .

a $p + 15 = 45$

$p + 15 - 15 = 45 - 15$

so $p = 30$

b $3y = 36$

$3y \div 3 = 36 \div 3$

so $y = 12$

c $4p + 3 = 27$

$4p + 3 - 3 = 27 - 3$

$4p = 24$

so $p = 6$

Copy and complete the crossnumber, using the solutions to the equations below.

Across

$a + 6 = 10$

$20 + 2c = 70$

$d + 45 = 100$

$h + 20 = 182$

$i + 50 = 295$

$2k - 3 = 45$

$2p = 3500$

$2u + 4 = 70$

$2t + 200 = 1000$

Down

$2b + 4 = 34$

$2e + 4 = 110$

$3f - 4 = 44$

$3g - 6 = 90$

$4j + 2 = 90$

$2m - 2 = 80$

$2n + 6 = 120$

$2q = 80$

$2r + 4 = 52$

$3s - 50 = 100$

$3v - 9 = 30$

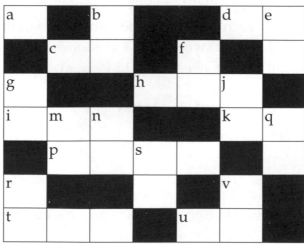

4e Balancing equations 2

example

Solve the following equations.

a $t + t + t + t + 5 = t + t + 11$ **b** $5g + 6 = 3g + 16$

. . . .

a $t + t + \cancel{t} + \cancel{t} + 5 = \cancel{t} + \cancel{t} + 11$ **b** $5g + 6 = 3g + 16$

(take $2t$ from both sides)   (take $3g$ from both sides)

$\qquad\quad 2t + 5 = 11$ $2g + 6 = 16$

(take 5 from both sides)   (take 6 from both sides)

$\qquad\qquad 2t = 6$ $2g = 10$

(divide both sides by 2)   (divide both sides by 2)

$\qquad\qquad\quad t = 3$ $g = 5$

1 Find the value of ⚲ on each set of scales.

a ⚲⚲⚲+5 ⚲⚲+12

b ⚲⚲⚲+5 ⚲+11

c ⚲+14 ⚲⚲+8

2 Solve each of these equations.

a $3b + 14 = 2b + 16$ **b** $5c + 4 = 3c + 22$ **c** $2d + 3 = d + 7$

d $4e + 2 = 2e + 16.$ **e** $3f + 11 = 5f + 3$ **f** $5g - 1 = 2g + 14$

g $9h + 4 = 5h + 20$ **h** $5i - 10 = i + 2$ **i** $2j + 11 = j + 20$

3 David and Teresa each have the same number of sweets.
David has 4 full bags of sweets and 3 loose sweets.
Teresa has 3 full bags of sweets and 15 loose sweets.

a Form an equation from the above information.

b Solve the equation to find out how many sweets there are in one full bag.

4f Writing equations

Jean has £145 in her bank account . She earns £p working in the local shop. She now has £210.

Write an equation and solve it to find how much money, £p, Jean earned.

· ·

$145 + p = 210$ (*take away 145 from both sides*)

$\qquad p = 65$

So she earned £65 working in the shop.

1 i If the perimeter of each shape is 36 cm, write an equation for the perimeter of each shape.

ii Solve your equations and use them to find the lengths of the sides of each shape.

a

$4x$

$2x$ ☐ $2x$

$4x$

b $3x+1$ ◺ $2x-2$

$\qquad 2x+2$

c $4x+8$

$3x$ ⬡ $3x$

$2x-2$

2 Write an equation for each of these stories.
Solve your equations to answer the questions.
Remember to show your workings.

a Gina has £y in her purse.
She spends £12. She is left with £13.
How much money did Gina have at the start?

b A puppy is x kg and it gains 5 kg in 6 months. The puppy's mass is now 10 kg.
What was the puppy's mass 6 months earlier?

c It costs £d to go to the cinema. Frank pays for 5 people to go to the cinema. The total cost of the 5 tickets was £22.50.
How much did each ticket cost?

d A bag of n sweets is shared between 6 people. Each person gets 5 sweets.
How many sweets were in the bag?

Do the following data come from primary or secondary data?
a Weather forecasts from the news
b Recording the amount of rainfall in your garden over a week

. . . .

a Secondary data – someone else has collected it.
b Primary data – you have collected it.

1 Persharan wants to encourage more people to visit her restaurant.
Do you think each of these suggestions is good idea or a bad idea?
Explain your answers.
a '2 for 1 offer Monday to Friday before 5 pm'
b '2 for 1 offer Saturday evening'
c 'Free balloons for under 7s'
d 'Children under 5 eat free'
e New decoration and signs outside
f Advertisements in the local newspapers with a free dessert voucher.

2 Simon wants to collect some data for a school project. He makes a
list of the data-collecting tasks he will do.
Do the data come from primary or secondary sources?
a BBC website
b Questionnaires given to a sample of 30 people
c An interview with a local shop-keeper
d Old newspapers kept in the library
e Recording the number of people who visit the museum each day.

example

Criticise and then re-write the following questions:
1. How old are you?   10–15   15–20   20+
2. How much money do you spend on music?
   Under £20   £30–£50   Loads

. . . .

1 The question is ok, but the options aren't: 15 is in two groups, the last group needs to be split up into smaller groups and it doesn't include all ages. The question could say
How old are you:
Under 10   10–19   20–29   30–39   40–49   50–59   60+

2 The question needs to ask over what period of time people spend this money, i.e. a week, month or year? It also needs to include all of the possible amounts whereas at the moment it leaves gaps. What does 'Loads' mean?! The question could read:
How much money do you spend on music on average in a month?
<£10   £10–£19   £20–£29   £30–£39   £40–£49   £50+

1 Criticise and then re-write the following questions.
   a How old are you?   Young   Old   Very old
   b How much money do you earn?
      Not much   About average   Quite a lot   Loads
   c What is your favourite food?
   d How much exercise do you do?
      None   1 hour   2 hours   3 hours   4+ hours

2 Pick one of the topics below and write your own questionnaire.
   – Healthy eating and exercise
   – Favourite hobbies, sports and activities
   – Views on what makes a good theme park, playground or arcade for children
   – your own idea.

example

The ages of 40 diners at Pesharan's restaurant are collected. Decide the size of each class and group the data into a frequency table.

31	34	22	36	45	35	35	56	12	45	34	31	23	25
56	46	61	34	56	43	41	45	27	46	39	41	56	61
19	35	7	45	28	58	15	60	35	51	51	50		

Ages of diners	Tally	Frequency
0–10	|	1
11–20	|||	3
21–30	⦀⦀	5
31–40	⦀⦀ ⦀⦀|	11
41–50	⦀⦀ ⦀⦀|	11
51–60	⦀⦀||	7
60+	||	2

1 Students in a Year 9 class were asked what their favourite sport is. The results were:

Football	Football	Netball	Football	Football	Rugby
Cricket	Football	Rugby	Netball	Cricket	Swimming
Netball	Tennis	Football	Rugby	Football	Badminton
Football	Badminton	Rugby	Football	Netball	Cricket
Swimming	Tennis				

a Draw a suitable frequency table.

b Tally the data into the frequency table.

c Which sport is the class favourite?

2 Collect some of your own data similar to the examples above and complete a frequency table to show your results.

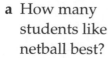

example

The bar chart shows the results from a class survey about favourite sports.

a How many students like netball best?

b Which sport is the modal favourite?

c Which sport did only 2 students like?

d How many students were in the class?

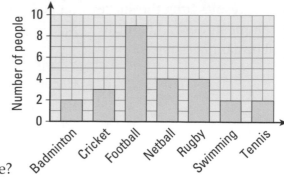

· ·

a Four students like netball best.

b Football is the modal favourite.

c Badminton, swimming and tennis were the favourite of only 2 students.

d $2 + 3 + 9 + 4 + 4 + 2 + 2 = 26$

There were 26 students in the class.

1 Diners at Persharan's restaurant were asked how much they had enjoyed their meal. The results are shown in the bar chart.

a How many said their meal was 'okay'?

b Which answer is the mode?

c What answer had the lowest frequency?

d How many people were surveyed?

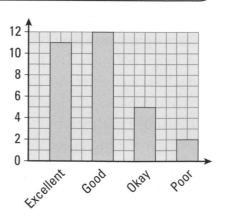

example

Draw a pie chart to show the results from the survey about students' favourite Humanities subject.

Humanities subjects	Tally	Frequency
Citizenship	IIII IIII	9
Geography	IIII IIII I	11
History	IIII III	8
Religious Education	IIII III	8

First add up the frequencies to find the total number of students.
$9 + 11 + 8 + 8 = 36$ students
Then divide 360° by the total frequency.
$360° \div 36 = 10°$ So 10° represents 1 student.

Humanities subjects	Angle
Citizenship	$9 \times 10° = 90°$
Geography	$11 \times 10° = 110°$
History	$8 \times 10° = 80°$
Religious Education	$8 \times 10° = 80°$

1 36 people were asked which of the five terrestrial channels they watch most often. The frequency table shows the results.

a Draw a circle about 10 cm in diameter.

b Using a protractor, draw the angles for each category.

c Colour code your chart, provide a key and a suitable title.

Terrestrial channel	Tally	Frequency
BBC1	IIII IIII II	12
BBC2	III	3
ITV	IIII IIII	10
Channel 4	IIII	5
Channel 5	I	1

2 Ask 18 people what their favourite type of TV programme is and draw a pie chart to represent your data.

example

Here are the shoe sizes of 10 students in Samuel's class.

4, 3.5, 5, 6, 6, 7, 3, 3, 6, 4.5

Find the **a** mode **b** median **c** mean.

· ·

First write the data in order.

3, 3, 3.5, 4, 4, 5, 6, 6, 6, 7

a The mode is 6.

b The median is the middle value, which is half-way between 4 and 5. The median is 4.5.

c $3 + 3 + 3.5 + 4 + 4 + 5 + 6 + 6 + 6 + 7 = 47.5$

$47.5 \div 10 = 4.75$. The mean is 4.75.

1 Find the **i** mode **ii** median **iii** mean, for each of these sets of data.

a 1, 7, 4, 3, 5, 8, 7

b 4, 7, 2, 4, 3, 2, 7, 7

c 4, 0, 2, 1, 0, 1, 12, 0, 3, 1, 0

d 2.5, 3.8, 2.5, 3.1, 4.2, 3.3, 2.5, 4.3

2 Persharan records the amount of money that is spent, to the nearest £, by customers on 15 tables during one evening. The results are as follows:

£34   £14   £29   £45   £12   £51   £14   £47   £51   £14   £15
£17   £23   £46   £26

Work out the **i** mode **ii** median **iii** mean amounts spent.

3 Naz and David each record the number of miles they drove each day.

	Mon	Tues	Wed	Thurs	Fri
Naz	21.5	32.6	41.8	9.7	11.6
David	33.8	36.7	36.5	91.2	3.2

a Work out the mean daily mileage.

b Find the median distance driven by each person.

c Explain why the mode would not be a useful average in this case.

5f Writing a statistical report

Persharan displays some of the data that she has collected in charts, tables and graphs. She must now prepare a report for the manager. In the report she needs to explain the findings of her investigation.

Customer satisfaction for 2008 and 2009

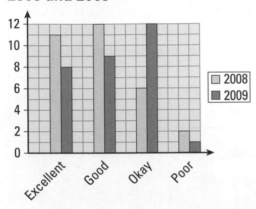

Age of customers

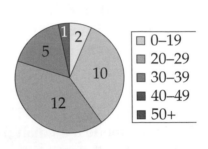

- 0–19
- 20–29
- 30–39
- 40–49
- 50+

1 What could Persharan use as a title for her report?

2 a Write a brief statement giving the reason for Persharan's investigation.

　b The comparison bar chart compares last year's customer satisfaction with the figures for this year.
　What does this tell Persharan about the experience her customers are having at her restaurant this year compared to last year?

3 To help improve her business Persharan wants to attract more customers. Use the pie chart to find
　a which age group is the mode
　b which age groups are the least common.
　c Which age groups do you think she should target, and why?

6a Metric measures

How many
i   centimetres are in 2.5 metres
ii millimetres are in 30 centimetres
iii tonnes are in 3500 kilograms
iv millilitres in 2 litres?

· ·

i $2.5 \times 100 = 250$ centimetre   ii $30 \times 10 = 300$ millimetres
iii $3500 \div 1000 = 3.5$ tonnes   iv $2 \times 1000 = 2000$ millilitres

1 How many
  a centimetres are there in 3.5 metres
  b millimetres are there in 25 centimetres
  c tonnes in 2700 kilograms
  d kilograms in 4500 grams?

2 a 1250 millilitres are poured from a 2-litre bottle. How much is left?
  b Two kilograms of peas are shared equally between 4 bags. How many grams of peas are there in each bag?
  c How many litres are there in total if you have 8 bottles, each containing 250 millilitres?

3 One lap of a running track is 400 metres. How many laps would Tristan need to run in order to complete
  a 1 mile (1 mile is 1.6 kilometres)?
  b 4 miles?
  c a marathon (approximately 26 miles)?

4 Convert these following metric measurements to Imperial measurements:
  a 4 litres is about .... pints.
  b 7 metres is about .... feet.
  c 250 grams is about .... ounces.
  d 10 metres is about .... yards and about .... feet.
  e 8 kilometres is about ..... miles.
  f 20 kilometres is about ... miles.

example

How many
a feet are there in 4 yards   b inches are there in 8 feet
c ounces are there in 5 pounds d   pounds are there in 5 stone?
. . . .
a $4 \times 3 = 12$ feet   b $8 \times 12 = 96$ inches
c $5 \times 16 = 80$ pounds   d $5 \times 14 = 70$ ounces

1 How many
   a feet are there in 7 yards?

   b inches are there in 12 feet?

   c ounces are there in 3.5 pounds?

   d pounds are there in 9 stone?

   e pints are there in 8 gallons?

2 Todd fills his motorbike with petrol. It will take 3 gallons.

   a How many pints is this?

   b How many litres is this, approximately?

3 Which is greater

   a 5 inches or 12 centimetres?

   b 10 pounds or 6 kilograms?

   c 160 centimetres or 5 feet?

   d 4 stones or 25 kilograms?

   e 10 pints or 6 litres?

   f 10 kilometres or 14 miles?

4 Convert these Imperial measurements into metric measurements.

   a 5 pounds of potatoes is about ... kilograms.

   b 10 pints of milk is about ... litres.

   c 5.5 yards of rope is about ... metres.

   d 10 miles is about ... kilometres.

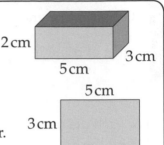

example

Calculate the volume of this cuboid.

To find the volume count the cubes.
- There will be 15 centimetre cubes on each layer.
- There are two layers.
- There are $15 + 15 = 30$ cubes altogether.

2 cm
3 cm
5 cm
5 cm
3 cm

1 Calculate the area of each of these rectangles.

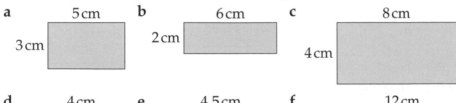

a 5 cm 3 cm

b 6 cm 2 cm

c 8 cm 4 cm

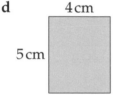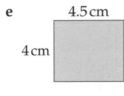

d 4 cm 5 cm

e 4.5 cm 4 cm

f 12 cm 2.5 cm

2 Calculate the area of each of these.
Take care to use the correct units.
  a A picture frame is 40 cm wide by 50 cm long.
  b A sheet of cardboard is 25 cm by 50 cm
  c A carpet is 8 foot by 12 foot.
  d A swimming pool is 25 metres by 12 metres.

3 Find the volume of each of these cuboids.

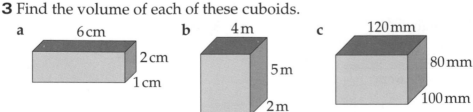

a 6 cm 2 cm 1 cm

b 4 m 5 m 2 m

c 120 mm 80 mm 100 mm

example

Calculate the area of the triangle.

Area of triangle $= \frac{1}{2} \times$ base $\times$ height

$\qquad = \frac{1}{2} \times 12 \times 4 = 24\,\text{cm}^2$

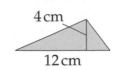

1 For each diagram

  i find the area of the rectangle

  ii find the area of the enclosed triangle.

a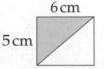

b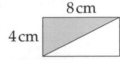

c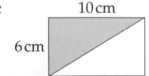

2 Calculate the area of each of these triangles.

a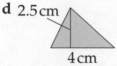

b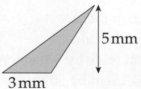

c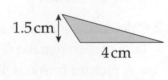

d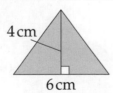

e

f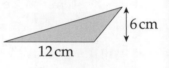

3 Carefully draw and measure these triangles.
Calculate the area.

a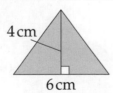

b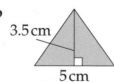

example

Calculate the area of these shapes.

a   6 cm

3 cm

b   4 cm

2 cm

7 cm

· ·

a Area $= b \times h$
$= 6\,\text{cm} \times 3\,\text{cm}$
$= 18\,\text{cm}^2$

b Area $= \frac{1}{2} \times (a + b) \times h$
$= \frac{1}{2} \times (4\,\text{cm} + 7\,\text{cm}) \times 2\,\text{cm}$
$= \frac{1}{2} \times 11\,\text{cm} \times 2\,\text{cm}$
$= 11\,\text{cm}^2$

1 Calculate the area of these parallelograms by either counting squares or using the formula.

a   b 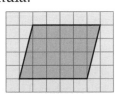   c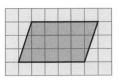

2 Calculate the area of these trapezium by either counting squares or using the formula.

a   b 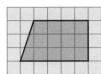   c

3 Jonny worked out the area of this parallelogram, but he has made a mistake.
What did Jonny do wrong?
Area $= b \times h$
$= 5\,\text{cm} \times 3\,\text{cm} = 15\,\text{cm}^2$

3 cm   2 cm
←5 cm→

example

Calculate the volume of this cuboid.

Volume of a cuboid
= length × width × depth
= 5 cm × 3 cm × 2 cm = 30 cm³

2 cm
3 cm
5 cm

1 Find the volume of each of these cuboids using the formula.
Volume $= l \times w \times d$

a
3 cm
2 cm
4 cm

b
4 cm
3 cm
5 cm

c
3 cm
4 cm
5 cm

d
5 cm
4 cm
6 cm

e
4 cm
8 cm
6 cm

2 A tank is used to collect rainwater. The tank is 3 feet wide, 4 feet long and 6 feet deep. What is the volume of the water if the tank is:
i completely full   **ii** only a third full?

3 Bricks measure 15 cm long, 7 cm high and 4 cm deep. Thirty bricks are used to build a small wall.
  a What is the volume of the wall?

  A wall is built using a single layer.
  The wall is 150 cm long and 35 cm high.
  b What is the volume of the wall?
  c How many bricks would have been used to make it?

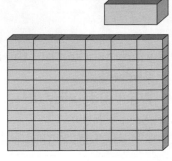

The circumference of a circle is the distance around its edge.
The diameter of a circle is the distance across the circle, through its centre.

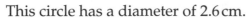

This circle has a diameter of 2.6 cm.
This circle has a circumference of 8.2 cm.

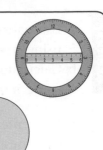

1 Measure the circumference and diameter of 10 different circular objects around the house, e.g. a tin of beans, a bucket, coke can or a two-pence piece. If you can't find 10 objects, draw 10 circles of different sizes with a pair of compasses.

a Record your measurements into a table like the one below.

Object	Diameter (cm)	Circumference (cm)	Circumference ÷ diameter
Tin of beans			

b Complete the last column by dividing each circumference by the diameter.

c What do you notice about your results?

2 Using what you found in question 1, state which of these circles you think was not measured correctly. Explain your answer.

a Diameter = 13 cm   Circumference = 41 cm

b Diameter = 8 cm   Circumference = 28 cm

c Diameter = 5.5 cm   Circumference = 17.4 cm

example

a Estimate the circumference of this circle using π ≈ 3

b Calculate the circumference of this circle using π ≈ 3.1

· ·

a Circumference = 3 × 12 = 36 cm

b Circumference = 3.1 × 12 = 37.2 cm

12 cm

1 Estimate the circumference of each of these circles using π ≈ 3.

a
10 cm

b
6.5 cm

c
18 mm

d
25 cm

e
12.5 m

f
45 mm

2 Calculate the circumference of each of the above circles using π ≈ 3.1.

3 A windmill's blades rotate so that the tips make a circle.
  a If each blade is 5 metres long, how far will each tip travel in one full revolution? Use π ≈ 3.
  b On a very windy day the blade tips travel a total of 24 800 metres. How many full revolutions did the blades make?

4 A bike wheel has a diameter of 90 cm.
Using π ≈ 3, work out:
  a the distance the bike will travel in one full revolution;
  b how many revolutions would be needed for the bike to travel
  i 1350 cm   **ii** 54 metres?

example

Complete these calculations.
a 40×0.1 **b** 6000×0.01 **c** $35 \div 0.1$ **d** $450 \div 0.01$

. . . .

a $40 \times \frac{1}{10}$ **b** $6000 \times \frac{1}{100}$ **c** $35 \div \frac{1}{10}$ **d** $450 \div \frac{1}{100}$
$ = 40 \div 10$ $= 6000 \div 100$ $= 35 \times 10$ $= 450 \times 100$
$ = 4$ $= 60$ $= 350$ $= 45\,000$

1 Multiply each of these numbers by 10.

a 67	**b** 15	**c** 70	**d** 130
e 3.4	**f** 4.9	**g** 0.5	**h** 1.2
i 0.02	**j** 12.01	**k** 0.003	**l** 0.045

2 Divide each of these numbers by 10.

a 100	**b** 40	**c** 250	**d** 3000
e 1120	**f** 540	**g** 54	**h** 15
i 2.5	**j** 25.6	**k** 4.1	**l** 0.11

3 Multiply each of these numbers by 100.

a 23	**b** 60	**c** 120	**d** 200
e 1000	**f** 123	**g** 1.2	**h** 0.4
i 0.03	**j** 51.1	**k** 0.0034	**l** 1.001

4 Divide each of these numbers by 100.

a 500	**b** 2500	**c** 120	**d** 200 000
e 1270	**f** 55	**g** 408	**h** 2950
i 1.2	**j** 0.09	**k** 1.23	**l** 23.8

5 Copy and complete these calculations with either 0.1 or 0.01.

a $9 \times \square = 0.9$ **b** $13 \times \square = 1.3$ **c** $4 \div \square = 40$
d $123 \div \square = 12\,300$ **e** $2004 \times \square = 20.04$ **f** $3.4 \div \square = 34$
g $99 \times \square = 0.99$ **h** $10.01 \div \square = 100.1$ **i** $0.074 \div \square = 7.4$

example

Use a number line to round each of these numbers.
a 6.7 to the nearest integer   **b** 34 to the nearest 10
c 450 to nearest 100   **d** 3099 to nearest 1000

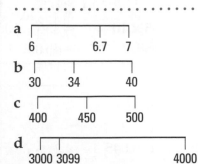

a 6   6.7   7   6.7 is closer to **7**

b 30   34   40   34 is closer to **30**

c 400   450   500   450 is half-way between
                                            400 and 500, so round up to **500**

d 3000 3099   4000   3099 is closer to **3000**

1 Round each of these numbers to the nearest integer (whole number).

a 3.6	**b** 9.2	**c** 4.5	**d** 12.1
e 8.7	**f** 19.9	**g** 39.2	**h** 99.9

2 Round each of these numbers to the nearest 10.

a 46	**b** 31	**c** 35	**d** 7
e 145	**f** 1291	**g** 97	**h** 4136

3 Round each of these numbers to the nearest 100.

a 1440	**b** 2399	**c** 3819	**d** 1250
e 97	**f** 2821	**g** 11 650	**h** 9999

4 Shannon is doing her maths homework using a calculator and her teacher has told her to round all of her answers to the nearest integer. Round each of these answers to the nearest integer.

a  **b**  **c**   **d**

45.3   123.99   4591.4   19.99

e   **f**  **g**   **h**

123.084   3.1453   85.055   121.905

example

Complete this calculation $\qquad 4^2 + (4+3) \times 3 - 5$

. . . .

First work out the **Brackets**:	$= 4^2 + 7 \times 3 - 5$	Brackets
Next work out the **Indices**:	$= 16 + 7 \times 3 - 5$	Indices
		Division
Next work out the **Multiplication**:	$= 16 + 21 - 5$	Multiplication
Next work out the **Addition**		Addition
and **Subtraction**:	$= 32$	Subtraction

1 Work out these using the correct order of operations.

    a $3 + 4 \times 5$ **b** $21 \div 3 + 2$ **c** $12 \times (4 + 3)$

    d $3^2 + 3 \times 2$ **e** $(4 \times 3) \div 2$ **f** $4^2 + 3 \times 2$

2 Use a calculator to work these out.

    a $(34 + 5) \times 14$ **b** $457 - (132 + 23)$ **c** $27 \times (94 - 59)$

    d $(23 - 6) \times (56 \div 8)$ **e** $19 + (14 \times 83) - 3^2$ **f** $(33 + 39) + 35 \times 4^2$

3 Work these out.

    a $36 \div (7 - 1) \times 3$ **b** $19 - (2 + 1) \div 4$ **c** $70 - (5 \times 6) + 4^2$

    d $6^2 + (16 \div 8) \times 3 + 1$ **e** $200 - (3 + 2^2 \times 5)$ **f** $(4 + 6) \times 5^2 - (5 + 1)$

4 Add the brackets, where necessary, to these calculations to make them correct.

    a $4 \times 2 + 6 = 32$

    b $15 - 5 \times 6 - 3 = 0$

    c $125 - 5^2 \times 4 = 25$

    d $5 + 4^2 - 6 - 2 = 17$

    e $15 - 2^2 + 12 \div 4 + 4^2 = 27$

7d Addition and subtraction

Work out the following by writing the calculations in columns.

a $234 + 56 + 178$ **b** $12.8 - 3.3$

```
a  2 | 3 | 4          b  1 | ¹2 • 8
     | 5 | 6                 | 3 • 3
   1 | 7 | 8                 | 9 • 5
   4 | 6 | 8
   1     1
```

1 Use a number line to work out these calculations.

  a $45 + 34$ **b** $67 + 12$ **c** $35 + 26$

  d $58 + 34$ **e** $24 + 49$ **f** $121 + 34$

2 Use a number line to work out these calculations.

  a $45 - 23$ **b** $65 - 12$ **c** $98 - 35$

  d $67 - 58$ **e** $123 - 87$ **f** $143 - 68$

3 Work these out by writing the calculations in columns.

  a $245 + 34$ **b** $65 + 88$ **c** $239 + 34$

  d $123 + 16 + 39$ **e** $435 + 356 + 78$ **f** $376 + 587 + 39$

4 Work out these by writing the calculations in columns.

  a $85 - 34$ **b** $78 - 27$ **c** $123 - 16$

  d $84 - 45$ **e** $147 - 89$ **f** $426 - 257$

5 Work out these calculations.

  a $4.3 + 6.2$ **b** $7.3 + 13.2$ **c** $23.8 + 13.4$

  d $145.7 + 23.5$ **e** $9.8 + 342.9$ **f** $4.9 + 0.7 + 45$

6 Work out these calculations.

  a $6.8 - 3.4$ **b** $35.7 - 23.5$ **c** $120.4 - 45.1$

  d $67.4 - 35.7$ **e** $143.6 - 59.8$ **f** $304 - 58.5$

example

Work out
a 17×8 **b** $84 \div 6$

· ·

a 17×8
$= (10 + 7) \times 8$
$= (10 \times 8) + (7 \times 8)$
$= 80 + 56 = 136$
Answer: $17 \times 8 = 136$

b $\begin{array}{r} \overline{)84} \\ -\ 60 \quad 10 \times 6 \\ \hline 24 \\ -\ 24 \quad 4 \times 6 \\ \hline 0 \quad 14 \end{array}$ Answer: $84 \div 6 = 14$

1 Work out the following calculations in your head.
a 6×5 **b** 8×4 **c** 12×4 **d** 9×4
e 8×7 **f** 9×6 **g** 12×5 **h** 11×11
i 7×4 **j** 6×8 **k** 8×9 **l** 3×7

2 Work out the following calculations in your head.
a 3×10 **b** $130 \div 10$ **c** 34×100 **d** $420 \div 10$
e 35×100 **f** $96 \div 10$ **g** $400 \div 100$ **h** 3.2×100
i 0.9×100 **j** 37×10 **k** $0.4 \div 100$ **l** $12.3 \div 100$

3 Use partitioning to work out these multiplications.
Make estimates of your answers before you start each calculation.
a 4×19 **b** 18×5 **c** 4×32 **d** 7×34
e 23×8 **f** 27×4 **g** 26×6 **h** 53×4

4 Use chunking (repeated subtraction) to work out these divisions.
Make an estimate of your answer before you start each calculation.
a $128 \div 8$ **b** $153 \div 9$ **c** $108 \div 6$ **d** $115 \div 5$
e $270 \div 15$ **f** $156 \div 12$ **g** $182 \div 14$ **h** $725 \div 25$

example

Work out 152×18 using these two methods:

i grid

ii column.

i

	100	50	2
10	1000	500	20
8	800	400	16

$$1520 + \\ 1216 \over 2736$$

ii

```
      1  5  2
         1  8  ×
    1  2  1  6
         4  1
    1  5  2  0
    2  7  3  6
```

Answer: $152 \times 18 = 2736$

Answer: $152 \times 18 = 2736$

1 Use the grid method to work out these.

a 14×13	**b** 13×384	**c** 15×218	**d** 18×242
e 167×18	**f** 26×178	**g** 254×24	**h** 36×175
i 245×24	**j** 367×34	**k** 27×365	**l** 145×236

2 Use the column method to work these out.

a 17×16	**b** 342×16	**c** 274×17	**d** 324×19
e 238×14	**f** 423×24	**g** 346×26	**h** 19×274
i 23×435	**j** 376×41	**k** 34×367	**l** 845×23

3 Use your prefered method to work these out.

a 4×33.4	**b** 7×13.4	**c** 8×45.1	**d** 6×34.2
e 8×34.2	**f** 4×40.9	**g** 8×51.9	**h** 23×45.4
i 31×24.9	**j** 37×28.5	**k** 398×34.5	**l** 29.4×349

example

Work out $448 \div 16$

....

Work out the quotient by subtraction:

$$
\begin{array}{r}
16 \overline{)448} \\
-160 \quad 10 \times 16 \\
\hline
288 \\
-160 \quad 10 \times 16 \\
\hline
128 \\
-128 \quad 8 \times 16 \\
\hline
0 \quad 28
\end{array}
$$
Answer: $448 \div 16 = 28$

1 Do these calculations in your head as quickly as you can.

  a $24 \div 8$ **b** $36 \div 6$ **c** $45 \div 9$ **d** $56 \div 7$

  e $27 \div 3$ **f** $144 \div 12$ **g** $35 \div 7$ **h** $48 \div 8$

  i $72 \div 12$ **j** $54 \div 9$ **k** $32 \div 8$ **l** $108 \div 9$

2 Use a suitable method to work these out.

  a $64 \div 4$ **b** $78 \div 3$ **c** $128 \div 8$ **d** $138 \div 6$

  e $210 \div 6$ **f** $224 \div 8$ **g** $203 \div 7$ **h** $324 \div 9$

  i $238 \div 7$ **j** $348 \div 6$ **k** $162 \div 3$ **l** $476 \div 7$

3 Use a suitable method to work out these more difficult problems.

  a $345 \div 15$ **b** $384 \div 16$ **c** $816 \div 12$ **d** $360 \div 15$

  e $1134 \div 21$ **f** $442 \div 17$ **g** $552 \div 23$ **h** $364 \div 13$

  i $735 \div 21$ **j** $504 \div 21$ **k** $750 \div 30$ **l** $1464 \div 24$

7h Using a calculator

Calculate $\sqrt{2025} + 15$

Use your calculator.

$\sqrt{}$ (2 0 2 5) + 1 5 = [60]

1 Use a calculator to work these out, using the x^2 or $\sqrt{}$ button where required. Give your answers to 2 decimal places where appropriate.

a $9 + 2.6^2$

b $11 + 4.1^2$

c $5.8^2 \times 4$

d $1.8^2 - 0.95$

e $3.4 \times \sqrt{15.21}$

f $\sqrt{18 - 3}$

g $\sqrt{12 + 16}$

2 Suzanne has a 12 m length of tape and she wants to cut it into equal lengths of 250 cm. How many lengths will she make and what length will be left over?

3 There are 522 people on a cross channel ferry and all of them have ordered lunch. If the restaurant on board has 180 seats how many sittings will be required? How many people will there be at the last sitting if the others are full?

4 A garden centre has 570 kg of compost left in stock and the manager shares it out between 24 regular customers. How much will each customer receive? Express your answer in both fraction and decimal form.

54   **Number** Using a calculator

example

For the function $y = 2x + 1$ draw a function machine and complete the table of values.

Input

x
0
1
2
3
4
5

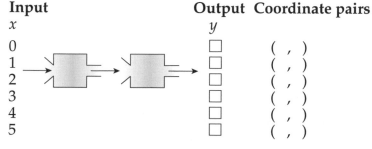

Output

y
1
3
5
7
9
11

Coordinate pairs

(0, 1)
(1, 3)
(2, 5)
(3, 7)
(4, 9)
(5, 11)

x	0	1	2	3	4	5
y	1	3	5	7	9	11

1 For the function $y = 3x + 2$ draw a function machine and complete the table of values.

Input

x
0
1
2
3
4
5

Output

y
☐
☐
☐
☐
☐
☐

Coordinate pairs

(,)
(,)
(,)
(,)
(,)
(,)

2 For each function draw a function machine and complete the table of values.

a $y = x + 1$ **b** $y = 2x + 5$ **c** $y = 5x + 2$ **d** $y = 4x - 3$ **e** $y = 6x - 3$

x	0	1	2	3	4	5
y						

3 Copy and complete this table of values for the relationship $y = x^2 + 3$.

x	0	1	2	3	4	5	6	7	8	9	10
x^2											
+3	+3	+3	+3	+3	+3	+3	+3	+3	+3	+3	+3
y											

example

Here is a table of values for the relationship $y = 2x + 1$.

x	0	1	2	3	4	5
y	1	3	5	7	9	11

i Plot the coordinates onto a set of axes.

ii Join the points to make a straight line.

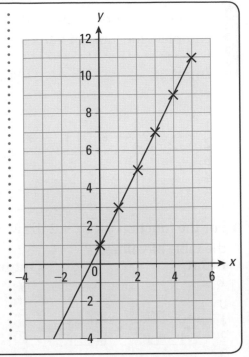

1 For each of the following relationships:

i complete a table of values

ii plot the coordinates onto a suitable set of axes

iii join the points with a straight line.

a $y = x + 2$ **b** $y = 3x + 1$

c $y = 4x + 2$ **d** $y = 5x$

e $y = 2x + 4$ **f** $y = 3x + 4$

2 For the relationship $y = x^2 + 2$:

a copy and complete the table of values

b plot the coordinates onto a suitable set of axes

c join the points with a smooth curve.

x	0	1	2	3	4	5
x^2						
$+2$	$+2$	$+2$	$+2$	$+2$	$+2$	$+2$
y						

Copy and complete the table of values for the relationship $y = 3x - 2$.

x	-3	-2	-1	0	1	2	3
y							

Plot the points onto a set of axes.

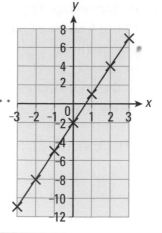

x	-3	-2	-1	0	1	2	3
y	-11	-8	-5	-2	1	4	7

1 a Copy and complete the table of values for the relationship $y = 2x - 3$.

x	-3	-2	-1	0	1	2	3
y			-5				

b Copy the axes.

c Plot the coordinates from the table.

d Join the points with a straight line.

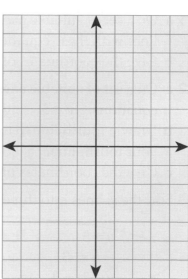

2 For each of the following relationships:

i complete a table of values as in question 1

ii plot the coordinates onto a suitable set of axes

iii join the points with a straight line.

   a $y = 2x - 1$ **b** $y = 3x - 1$

   c $y = 4x - 2$ **d** $y = 3x - 3$

   e $y = 2x - 4$ **f** $y = 3x - 4$

example

a On a set of suitable axes, draw the rectangle made from the four lines with these equations

$y = 4$ $y = -2$ $x = 3$ $x = -2$

b Give the coordinates where the lines cross.

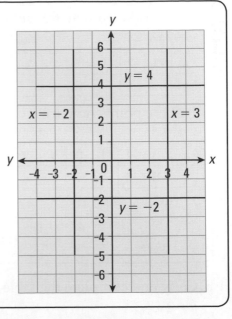

. . . .

b (-2, 4), (3, 4), (3, -2), (-2, -2)

1 a On a set of suitable axes, draw the rectangle made from the four lines with these equations: $y = 3$ $y = -5$ $x = 4$ $x = -2$
   b Give the coordinates of the point where the lines cross.

2 a On a set of suitable axes draw the three lines with these equations: $y = 5$ $y = -3$ $x = -4$
   b Draw a fourth line to make a square. What is the equation of your fourth line?
   c Give the coordinates of the points where the lines cross.

3 Sort these lines into three groups using the table below.

$y = 5$ $x = 3$ $y = 4$ $y = 2x$
   $x = -3$ $y = 1$ $y = 0$ $x = 3$
$y = 2x + 1$ $x = -3$ $x = 0$ $y = 3x - 2$

Horizontal	Vertical	Neither horizontal or vertical

8e Straight-line rules

a For the line $y = 3x + 2$ write the rule that links the x and y coordinates. Use a function machine if necessary.

b Copy and complete this sentence.
'The points on the line move .... squares up for every one square across.'

· ·

a The x value is multiplied by three and then 2 is added.

$$x \longrightarrow \boxed{\times 3} \longrightarrow \boxed{+2} \longrightarrow y$$

b 'The points on the line move three squares up for every one square across.'

1 For each of the following lines

i write the rule that links the x and y coordinate in the graph above using a function machine if necessary;

ii write the equation of the line $\quad y = ...$

a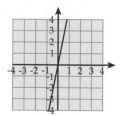
b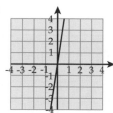
c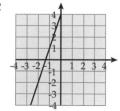

2 Without plotting points draw the following graphs:

a $y = 2x + 2$ **b** $y = 5x$ **c** $y = 3x + 3$ **d** $y = 4x + 5$

Here are some hints to help you.
First copy and complete this sentence: 'The points on the line move .... squares up for every one square across.'
- Start drawing the line where it crosses the y axis.

example

Anish is arranging marbles into a pattern.

a Make a table of values to record how the number of marbles changes with the pattern number.

pattern numbers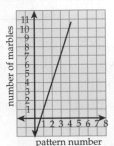

b Plot the values from the table on a graph and join the points with a straight line.

c Extend the line to find where it crosses the vertical axis.

d Use your answers to parts c and d to write the rule that connects the number of marbles with the pattern number.

· ·

a

Pattern number	1	2	3	4	5
Number of marbles	1	4	7	10	13

b

c The line crosses the *y* axis at -2.

d The number of marbles is three times the pattern number minus two.

1 Justin is building a fence. The fence posts make this pattern.

1 post   5 posts   9 posts   ...

a Make a table of values to record how the number of fence posts changes with the number of rectangles.

b Plot the values from your table on a graph and join the points with a straight line.

c Extend the line to find where it crosses the vertical axis.

d Copy and complete this sentence:
'The points move .... squares up for every one square across.'

e Use your answers to part c and d to write the rule that connects the number of rectangles with the number of fence posts.

example

The vase is being steadily filled with water
Which of the graphs shows the relationship
between time and height of water in the vase?

Height of water — Time

Height of water — Time

Height of water — Time

Graph 1 is the correct graph as the increase in the height of
water will slow down as time increases.

1 Here are three containers.
Water is poured into the
containers at a steady rate.
The graphs show depth of
water against time.

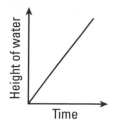
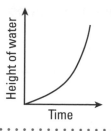

a   b   c

a Sketch the bottles and match
each one to the correct graph.

b Sketch a graph to show
depth of water against time
when this container is filled.

1   2   3

2 Faye takes her dog to the park for a
walk. This is her distance–time graph.

a What happens when she is
800 metres from home?

b How long does it take her to reach
the park?

c How long does she stay at the park?

d When was she walking slowest?

e How far did she walk in total?

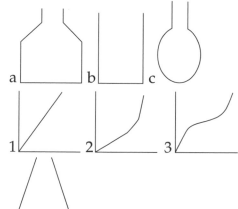

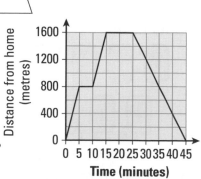

Distance from home (metres)

1600
1200
800
400
0

0 5 10 15 20 25 30 35 40 45
Time (minutes)

> Use a fraction to describe the probability of these events.
> **a** Getting a head when tossing a fair coin
> **b** Getting a 5 when rolling a fair dice
> **c** The spinner stopping on black
>
>
>
> ·
>
> **a** $\frac{1}{2}$ **b** $\frac{1}{6}$ **c** $\frac{1}{4}$

1 Decide which word best describes the probability of each event.
   a It will snow on Christmas Day.
   b You will get a tail if you toss a coin.
   c You will score a six if you roll a fair dice.
   d You will become a millionaire.
   e You will have homework tonight.
   f It will rain in October.

> Certain
> Likely
> Evens chance
> Unlikely
> Impossible

2 Use a fraction to describe the probability of these events.
   a The spinner stopping on 1   **b** Picking a black ball from the bag

   c Picking a card with an odd   **d** The spinner stopping on a
   number   prime number.

3 Copy this probability scale.
   Show the probabilities from question 2 on
   your scale. Add some more of your own.

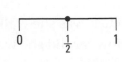

example

Trevor gets dressed in the dark. In his drawer he has two blue ties, three green ties and one red tie. He is wearing a pink shirt so doesn't want to wear a red tie.

a What is the probability he picks out a blue tie?
b What is the probability he picks out a green tie?
c What is the probability he picks out a blue tie or a green tie?
d What is the probability he picks out a red tie?

. . . .

a $\frac{2}{6} = \frac{1}{3}$ **b** $\frac{3}{6} = \frac{1}{2}$ **c** $\frac{5}{6}$ **d** $\frac{1}{6}$

1 Razia has a box of chocolates.
Nine of the chocolates are milk chocolate, six are plain chocolate and three are creams. Razia doesn't like creams. She doesn't look at the chocolates before picking them.
a What is the probability she picks a milk chocolate?
b What is the probability she picks a plain chocolate?
c What is the probability she picks a milk chocolate or a plain chocolate?
d What is the probability she picks one of the creams which she doesn't like?

2 Samantha is playing with her friends. Three of them want to play football, four of them want to go to the beach and one of them wants to play on the swings. They all put their suggestions on a piece of paper and put them in a hat. One idea is selected at random without looking.
a What is the probability that they go to the beach?
Samantha isn't allowed to go to the beach without telling her mum. Therefore, she wants to play at the park.
b What is the probability that they either play football or play on the swings?

example

A fair dice is rolled. What is the probability of rolling a multiple of 3?

· ·

Favourable outcomes: 3, 6

$P(\text{Multiple of 3}) = \dfrac{\text{number of favourable outcomes}}{\text{total number of outcomes}} = \dfrac{2}{6} = \dfrac{1}{3}$

1 Which of these jars give equally likely outcomes for choosing a black ball?

2 Find the probability of spinning an odd number on each of these spinners.

3 Use the formula to calculate these probabilities.

   a You roll a fair dice.
   What is the probability of rolling a prime number?

   b A bag contains three blue counters, one yellow counter and five red counters.
   A counter is picked at random.
   What is the probability of picking a counter that is not red?

   c A box contains three milk chocolates, four plain chocolates and three creams.
   A chocolate is picked at random.
   What is the probability of not picking a milk chocolate?

9c² Two events

example

A spinner is spun and a coin is tossed at the same time.
Complete a sample space diagram to show all of the possible outcomes.
How many different outcomes are there?

. . . .

		Spinner			
		1	2	3	4
Coin	Head	Head, 1	Head, 2	Head, 3	Head, 4
	Tails	Tail, 1	Tail, 2	Tail, 3	Tail, 4

There are eight different outcomes.

1 John has three shirts and two pairs of trousers.

 a Copy and complete the sample space diagram to show all of the possible combinations.

		Shirt		
		Blue	Green	Pink
Trousers	Black			
	Navy			

 b How many different combinations are there?

2 Trevor gets dressed in the dark. He has one pair each of black socks, navy socks and white socks.

 a Copy and complete the sample space diagram to show all of the different combinations for socks on his left and right foot.

		Right foot		
		Black	Navy	White
Left foot	Black			
	Navy			
	White			

 b How many possible ways are there for him to wear odd socks?

 c What is the probability he will not wear odd socks?

example

A biased dice is rolled 90 times. The results are recorded in the table below.

Number	1	2	3	4	5	6
Frequency	10	11	14	13	11	31

a Which number do you think the dice is biased towards? Why?

b What is the experimental probability of this number?

. . . .

a The dice is biased toward six as it occurred more than twice as many times as the other numbers.

b The probability of the dice landing on the six is $\frac{31}{90}$

1 A ball is rolled through the following maze and ends up at A, B, C, D or E.
At each junction it has a same chance of going either way.
Colette thinks the ball has an equal chance of ending up at A, B, C, D or E.

Claire thinks that there isn't an equal chance of the ball ending up at A, B, C, D or E.

She does an experiment to see if she is right. The results are as follows:

End point	A	B	C	D	E
Frequency	24	27	26	11	12

a What is the experimental probability of the ball ending up at
  i point A   ii point D?

b Who do you think is correct, Colette or Claire? Explain your answer.

The results of spinning a biased spinner are as follows:

Number	1	2	3	4
Frequency	20	15	15	50

a Which number is the spinner most likely to land on?

b What is the experimental probability of the spinner landing on the number one?

c If the spinner was spun 400 times, how many times would you expect it to land on the number one?

. . . .

a Number 4   b $\frac{20}{100} = \frac{1}{5}$ c $400 \div 5 = 80$

80 times

1 Five people play a game of cards 50 times.

The results of who wins are recorded below:

Number	Sharon	Isnat	Pauline	Carol	Qasim
Frequency	8	10	11	9	12

a Give the probabilities of each person winning the card game.

b Who do you think is the best at card games? Explain your answer.

2 A spinner is spun and the number on which the pointer lands is recorded.

The results are given in the table.

Number	1	2	3	4
Frequency	15	25	5	5

a Which number is the spinner most likely to land on?

b What is the experimental probability of the spinner landing on the number 4?

c If the spinner was spun 200 times, how many times would you expect it to land on the number

i 1   ii 2   iii 3   iv 4?

example

Rotate the triangle through 90° anticlockwise about (0,0).

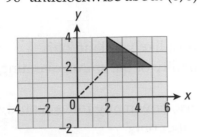

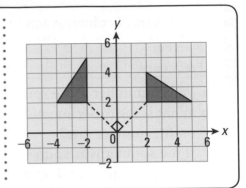

1 a Give the transformation that maps the shaded shape onto
  i A **ii** B **iii** C
  iv D **v** E.

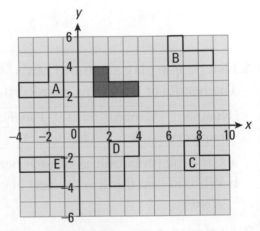

  b Give also the transformation that maps
  i D onto E
  ii E onto D
  iii A onto E
  iv A onto D
  v B onto C.

3 Copy the diagram.

  a Draw a rotation of the rhombus through 90° about (0,0) (in either direction) onto your copy.

  b Your pattern should have an octagon around its centre. Is this octagon a regular one? If not, why not?

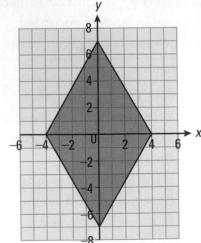

10b Reflection

example

a On a copy of the grid, reflect triangle ABC in the mirror line.
b Label the vertices of the image $A^1B^1C^1$.
c What is the equation of the mirror line?

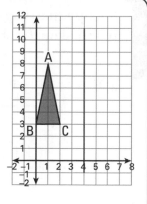

a, b

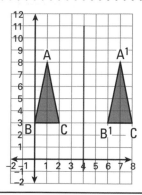

c $x = 4$

1 a Copy this diagram.
b Draw the mirror line on your diagram.
c What is the equation of the mirror line?
d Reflect triangle $A_1B_1C_1$ in the x axis. Label the image $A_2B_2C_2$.
e What are the coordinates of the vertices of triangle $A_2B_2C_2$?

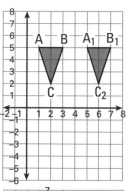

2 a Copy this diagram.
b Reflect rectangle ABCD in the mirror line. Label the vertices of the image $A^1B^1C^1D^1$.
c What is the equation of the mirror line?
d Reflect rectangle $A_1B_1C_1D_1$ in the y axis. Label the image $A_2B_2C_2D_2$.
e What are the coordinates of the vertices of rectangle $A_2B_2C_2D_2$?

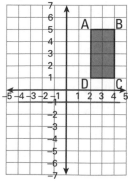

a Copy this diagram.
b Translate the shape using the vector $\begin{pmatrix} -5 \\ -2 \end{pmatrix}$

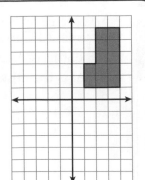

. . . .

a, b

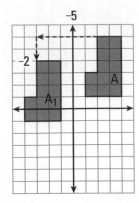

1 a Copy this diagram.
  b Draw the images of the translations
     of shape L by these vectors.

$L_1 : \begin{pmatrix} 2 \\ 2 \end{pmatrix}$ $L_2 : \begin{pmatrix} 5 \\ 3 \end{pmatrix}$

$L_3 : \begin{pmatrix} 4 \\ -2 \end{pmatrix}$ $L_4 : \begin{pmatrix} 6 \\ -5 \end{pmatrix}$

$L_5 : \begin{pmatrix} -1 \\ -7 \end{pmatrix}$ $L_6 : \begin{pmatrix} 0 \\ 3 \end{pmatrix}$

2 Use vectors to describe these translations.

  a A → B   **b** B → C
  c C → D   **d** D → E
  e E → F   **f** F → G

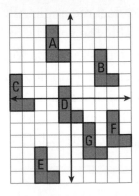

10d Rotation

example

Shape A has been rotated onto shape B.
a What are the coordinates of the centre of rotation?
b What is the direction of the rotation?
c Through how many degrees has the shape been turned?

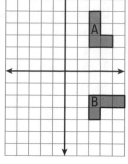

. . . .

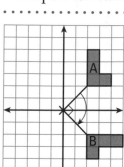

a (0,0) is the centre if the rotation.
(*Lines have been added to show the centre.*)
b Clockwise (*See the arrow*)
c 90° (*The angle between the lines is 90°.*)

1 Copy these diagrams.
Rotate the shapes about the centre of rotation marked on each diagram through the angle and direction given.

a

90° anticlockwise

b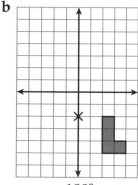

180°

c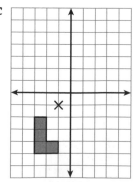

270° clockwise

example

a Enlarge this shape by a scale factor of 3.

b What is the scale factor that would reduce the large triangle to the small triangle?

a

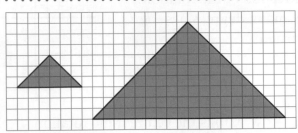

b A scale factor of $\frac{1}{3}$ would reduce the large triangle onto the smaller triangle.

1 Copy these shapes onto squared paper and enlarge them by the given scale factor.

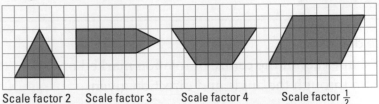

Scale factor 2   Scale factor 3   Scale factor 4   Scale factor $\frac{1}{2}$

2 What is the scale factor of enlargement or reduction from A to B in each of these diagrams?

a   **b**   **c**

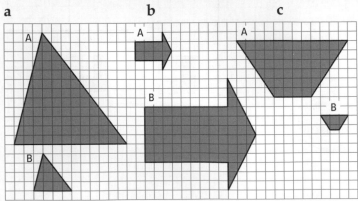

example

Copy this shape.
Use the ray lines to enlarge the
triangle by a scale factor of 2.

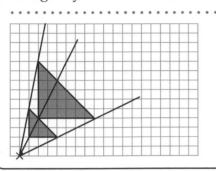

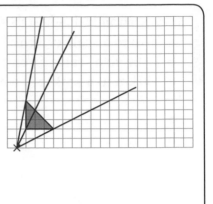

1 Copy each shape and enlarge by the given scale factor using the
ray lines.

a   Scale factor 3

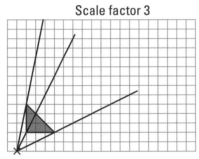

b   Scale factor 2

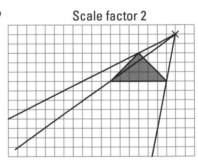

2 For each of the following questions work out the scale factor
of the enlargement from A to B.

a

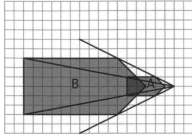

b

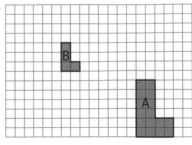

example

Draw straight lines to these scales.
a 30 m to a scale of 1 cm : 5 m
b 150 m to a scale of 1 cm : 15 m
c 350 km to a scale of 1 cm : 50 km

. . . .

a _____

b _____

c _____

1 Draw a straight line to each of these scales.
   a 40 m to a scale of 1 cm : 5 m   **b** 200 m to a scale of 1 cm : 50 m
   c 450 km to a scale of 1 cm : 50 km   **d** 48 m to a scale of 1 cm : 4 m
   e 18 km to a scale of 2 cm : 3 km   **f** 99 m to a scale of 2 cm : 33 m

2 The scale for this drawing is 1 cm : 6 m.
   The measurements have been left off the drawing.
   a Measure the length of each side of the shape to
      the nearest millimetre.
   b What are the sides of the real-life shape?

3 This is a sketch of Sanjay's bedroom.
   Draw a plan of Sanjay's room to a scale of
   4 cm : 1 m.

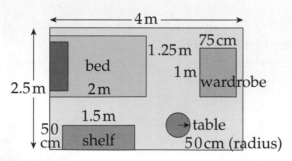

a Find the lowest common multiple (LCM) of 6 and 8.
b Find the highest common factor (HCF) of 24 and 36.

· ·

a Multiples of 6 are: 6, 12, 18, ⑳24, 30, 36, 42, 48, ...
Multiples of 8 are: 8, 16, ㉔24, 32, 40, 48, 56, 64, ...
24 is the lowest common multiple of 6 and 8.
b Factors of 24 are: 1, 2, 3, 4, 6, 8, ⑫12, 24
Factors of 36 are: 1, 2, 3, 4, 6, 9, ⑫12, 18, 36
12 is the highest common factor of 24 and 36.

1 List the first six multiples of
   a 5   **b** 6   **c** 12   **d** 15.

2 a Copy and complete these lists of the factors of 36 and 64.
   Factors of 36 are: 1, 36, 2, 18, ...
   Factors of 64 are: 1, 64, 2, 32, ...
  b What factors are common to 36 and 64?

3 a List the first few multiples of 4 and 6.
   Multiples of 4: 4, 8, ...
   Multiples of 6: 6, 12, ...
  b What is the lowest common multiple of 4 and 6?

4 Find the highest common factor (HCF) of
   a 9 and 12   **b** 24 and 36
   c 18 and 30   **d** 48 and 72.

5 Find the lowest common multiple (LCM) of
   a 4 and 6   **b** 8 and 7
   c 12 and 15   **d** 16 and 36.

example

Write these numbers as a product of their prime factors.

a 36   **b** 24

· ·

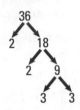
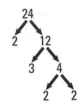

a $36 = 2 \times 2 \times 3 \times 3$ **b** $24 = 2 \times 2 \times 2 \times 3$

1 Test to see if these numbers are divisible by 3.

  a 42   **b** 51   **c** 91   **d** 108   **e** 133

2 Which of these numbers is divisible by both 3 and 5?

  a 35   **b** 55   **c** 90   **d** 105   **e** 53

3 Are these numbers prime?

  a 97   **b** 79   **c** 51   **d** 91   **e** 63

4 Write each of these numbers as a product of their prime factors.

  a 56   **b** 18   **c** 124   **d** 98   **e** 99

  f 54   **g** 108   **h** 1000   **i** 3200   **j** 8000

example

Complete these statements.
a $8^2 = \square \times \square = \square$ **b** $\sqrt{144} = \square$

....

a $8^2 = 8 \times 8 = 64$ **b** $\sqrt{144} = 12$ (because $12^2 = 144$)

1 Copy and complete these statements about square numbers.
a $4^2 = 4 \times \square = \square$ **b** $12^2 = 12 \times \square = \square$ **c** $5^2 = \square \times \square = \square$

2 Copy and compete these statements about square roots.
a $\sqrt{25} = \square$ **b** $\sqrt{121} = \square$ **c** $\sqrt{225} = \square$

3 Below is the graph of $y = x^2$.

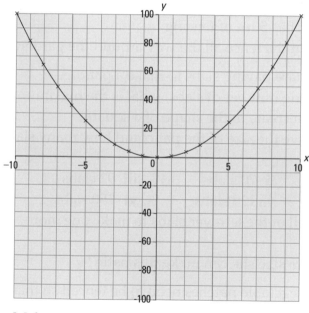

Make a copy of this graph and use it to
a estimate these square roots
i $\sqrt{40}$ **ii** $\sqrt{80}$ **iii** $\sqrt{95}$ **iv** $\sqrt{65}$ **v** $\sqrt{76}$
b estimate the value of these square numbers.
i 2.5^2 **ii** 6.5^2 **iii** 0.5^2 **iv** 7.8^2 **v** 9.4^2

11d Using square numbers and square roots

A square garden with an area of 25 m² is fenced.
a How long is each side of the garden?
b Sophie, the gardener, has 22 m of fencing.
Will she be able to put the fence all the way around the garden?
....

a $\sqrt{25} = 5$, so the length of each side is 5 m.
b A square has four equal sides so the distance around the garden is 5 m × 4 = 20 m, so Sophie has enough fencing.

1 A square garden with an area of 144 m² is fenced.
 a How long is each side of the garden?
 b Sophie, the gardener, has 50 m of fencing.
  Will she be able to put the fence all the way around the garden?

2 Sophie is arranging square paving slabs to make a patio.
 a If she has the following number of slabs, what is the maximum size of a patio she can create in the shape of a square?
  (For each question give the size of the patio and how many slabs will be left over.)

i 50 slabs	**ii** 70 slabs	**iii** 92 slabs
iv 105 slabs	**v** 120 slabs	**vi** 150 slabs

Sophie decides to use all of the leftover slabs to make one more square patio.
 b What is the maximum size she can make this patio?

3 The following square vegetable patches need to be fenced so that the rabbits cannot eat the vegetables.
Sophie knows the area of each vegetable patch.
Work out, by **rounding up** to the nearest metre, the length of fencing needed for each patch.
 a Area = 41 m²   **b** Area = 45 m²
 c Area = 69 m²   **d** Area = 93 m²

example

The perimeter of this shape is $4a + 5b$.
Find the length of the missing side.

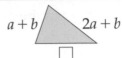

. . . .

$a + b + 2a + b = 3a + 2b$
You need a total of $4a + 5b$ so need another $a + 3b$.
The missing side has a length of $a + 3b$.

1 Simplify these expressions by collecting the terms.

a $i + i + i + i$ **b** $k + k + k + k + k$ **c** $b + b + 3b$

d $y + y + y + y + y - y$ **e** $3f + f + f - f$ **f** $m + 3m - m + 2m$

2 These expressions include two different terms.
Simplify them by collecting like terms together.

a $d + g + 2d + g$ **b** $3m + 2n + m + 2n + n$

c $5h + 3c - h + 2c - h$ **d** $7h + 3d - 5h + d + 2h$

e $2s + 3r - s + 5r + 4s$ **f** $4q + p + 3q + 4p - q$

3 Write an expression for the perimeter of each of these shapes.
Simplify your expression.

a

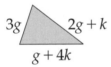

b

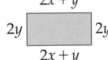

c

2q + 3p

p + q   p + q

2q

4 The perimeter of each of these shapes is $7a + 4b$.
Find the length of the missing side.

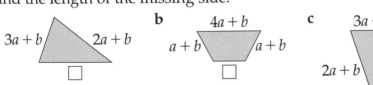

example

Multiply out the brackets in these expressions.
a $4(x + y)$ **b** $5(2x + 4y)$ **c** $3(5t - 7s)$

....

a $4(x + y)$ **b** $5(2x + 4y)$ **c** $3(5t - 7s)$
$= 4x + 4y$ $= 10x + 20y$ $= 15t - 21s$

1 The symbols represent the cost of each item on Clive's menu.
Write expressions, using brackets where necessary, for the cost
of these orders.

a 2 Bacon Baps and 2 Teas
b 3 Full Breakfasts and 3 Coffees
c 2 Egg on Toast and 2 Teas
d 4 Sausage Baps and 4 Coffees
e 2 Egg on Toast, 2 Sausage
Baps and 2 Teas
f 3 Bacon Baps, 3 Full Breakfasts
and 3 Coffees

Menu		
Bacon Bap	b	£1.30
Sausage Bap	s	£1.40
Egg on toast	e	£1.10
Full Breakfast	f	£3.00
Tea	t	£0.50
Coffee	c	£0.60

2 Substitute the prices of the items to find the cost of each order
in question 1. Show your working.
The first one is done for you.
a $2(b + t) = 2 \times (£1.30 + £0.50)$
$= 2 \times £1.80$
$= £3.60$

3 Multiply out the brackets in these expressions.
a $5(x + y)$ **b** $4(a - b)$ **c** $9(g + h)$
d $4(a + b + c)$ **e** $4(5t + 2s)$ **f** $3(2d + 3f)$
g $5(2w + 3v)$ **h** $2(4f - 2h)$ **i** $5(6y + 2z)$
j $4(12j - 2i)$ **k** $4(6w + 2x)$ **l** $7(3q + 2p)$

4 Multiply out the brackets and simplify these expressions.
a $3(d + 3e) + 2(2d + 2e)$ **b** $4(4g + 2h) + 3(2h + g)$
c $5(3c + 2b) + 2(5c + 3b)$ **d** $6(3a + 2b) + 2(2a + 4b)$

example

The formula for area A of a rectangle of length l and width w is:

$A = l \times w$ (l = length and w = width)

Use the formula to work out the area of these rectangles.

i $l = 4\,\text{cm}, w = 6\,\text{cm}$ **ii** $l = 2.5\,\text{cm}, w = 3\,\text{cm}$

. . . .

ii $A = l \times w$ **ii** $A = l \times w$

       $= 4 \times 6 = 24\,\text{cm}^2$ $= 2.5 \times 3 = 7.5\,\text{cm}^2$

1 a Use the formula above to work out the area of these rectangles.

     i $l = 2\,\text{cm}, w = 3\,\text{cm}$ **ii** $l = 5\,\text{cm}, w = 4\,\text{cm}$

     iii $l = 45\,\text{mm}, w = 20\,\text{mm}$ **iv** $l = 2.5\,\text{cm}, w = 10\,\text{cm}$

   b Rearrange the formula $A = l \times w$ so you can calculate the length, l, of a rectangle.

   c Use the rearranged formula to calculate the length of each of these rectangles.

     i $A = 50\,\text{cm}^2, w = 5\,\text{cm}$ **ii** $A = 72\,\text{cm}^2, w = 6\,\text{cm}$

     iii $A = 36\,\text{cm}^2, w = 4\,\text{cm}$ **iv** $A = 104\,\text{cm}^2, w = 8\,\text{cm}$

2 The formula for the volume V of a cuboid is $V = lwh$.

   (l = length, w = width and h = height)

   a Find the volume of a cuboid with $l = 5\,\text{cm}, w = 2\,\text{cm}, h = 3\,\text{cm}$.

   b Which of the following cuboids has the largest volume?

3 The voltage V in an electrical circuit, with current I and resistance R, is given by the formula $V = IR$.

   a What is V when $I = 6$ and $R = 8$?

   b What is R when $V = 56$ and $I = 8$?

example

The graph shows the temperature in a greenhouse recorded over a 7-hour period.

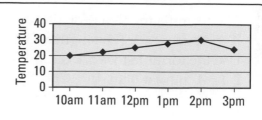

a What is the maximum temperature?

b After what time do you think the window was opened to lower the temperature inside the greenhouse?

· ·

a 30°C   b After 2 pm

---

1 The gas bills over a two-year period are collected.

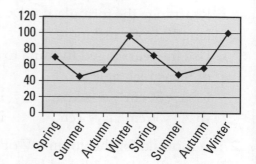

  a What time of year is the gas bill at its
     i greatest
     ii least?
  b How many times is the gas bill over £60?
  c Describe the pattern over the two years.
  d Are the gas bills increasing or decreasing over the two years?

2 This data records the temperature of a greenhouse over a day at 4-hour intervals.

  a Plot the data from the table onto suitable axes.
  b Join the points to make a straight line.
  c Describe what is happening to the temperature in the greenhouse over the whole day.

Time	Temperature (°C)
10 am	21
2 pm	32
6 pm	27
10 pm	19
2 am	10
6 am	12

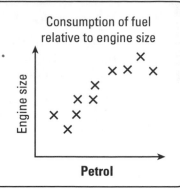

example

Describe the relationship shown on this scatter diagram.

· ·

The diagram shows that the bigger the engine size the more petrol a car uses.

Consumption of fuel relative to engine size

1 Ali measures the height and weight of ten students in a Year 7 class.

He records their heights on a scatter diagram.

a What is the link between a student's height and their weight?

Ali forgot to add one student, whose height is 165 cm.

b By looking at the diagram, what would you expect their weight to be?

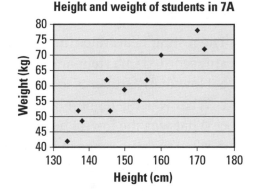

2 Describe the relationship shown on each of these scatter diagrams.

a

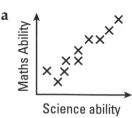

b

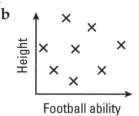

c

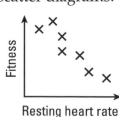

3 Collect the heights and weights of ten people and plot the data on a scatter graph. Describe any relationship.

example

Draw a stem-and-leaf diagram for these results of a maths test.

| 45 | 56 | 43 | 67 | 34 | 67 | 81 | 54 |
| 72 | 63 | 71 | 48 | 69 | 87 | 32 | 59 |

. . . .

```
3 | 2 4
4 | 3 5 4
5 | 4 6 9
6 | 3 7 7 6
7 | 12
8 | 17
```

Key: 5 | 9 Means 59%

1 The resting heart rates (in beats per minute) of a class of students are recorded in a stem-and-leaf diagram.

a How many students took part?

b What was the highest heart rate?

c What was the lowest heart rate?

d What was the range in heart rates?

e How many students had a heart rate between 70 and 79?

f What was the modal heart rate?

g What was the median heart rate?

```
4 | 3
5 | 4 5 5 6 7
6 | 0 3 3 4 4 5 9
7 | 2 2 3 4 5 5 5 5 7 8 8
8 | 0 0 1 1 4
9 | 2
```

2 The heart rates (in beats per minute) of the same students are collected after exercise. The data were as follows:

135, 120, 113, 88, 95, 98, 109, 105, 105, 111, 110, 112, 117, 114, 106, 108, 96, 112, 120, 123, 104, 105, 96, 112, 112, 131, 109, 140, 120

a Draw a stem-and-leaf diagram to represent these data.

b Use the stem-and-leaf diagram to work out the:

i highest heart rate   **ii** lowest heart rate

iii modal heart rate   **iv** median heart rate

v the range in heart rates.

12c² Frequency diagrams

The height, in metres, of 30 students is recorded below.
1.20, 1.54, 1.67, 1.45, 1.40, 1.65, 1.70, 1.56, 1.79, 1.34, 1.56, 1.67,
1.72, 1.39, 1.29, 1.39, 1.43, 1.56, 1.75, 1.29, 1.56, 1.40, 1.49, 1.71,
1.39, 1.29, 1.35, 1.39, 1.45, 1.49
Record these data in a frequency table.

Height in metres	Tally	Frequency
$1.20 \leq h \leq 1.30$	IIII	4
$1.30 \leq h \leq 1.40$	JHT I	6
$1.40 \leq h \leq 1.50$	JHT II	7
$1.50 \leq h \leq 1.60$	JHT	5
$1.60 \leq h \leq 1.70$	III	3
$1.70 \leq h \leq 1.80$	JHT	5

1 a Draw a frequency diagram for the data above. The axes are drawn for you.

b What is the modal class?

c How many of the students are over 1.50 m tall?

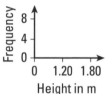

2 The weight of the 30 students were also recorded. Here are their weights in kg:

33, 56, 47, 39, 57, 45, 61, 62, 70, 56, 67, 39, 56, 35,
67, 64, 53, 59, 48, 53, 55, 61, 45, 64, 49, 69, 56, 58, 49

Use the data to find

a the range in weights

b the median weight.

c Group the data into a frequency table.

d Draw a frequency diagram for the weights.

1 The bar charts show how students travel to school during the summer term and winter term.

Summer term

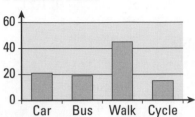

Winter term

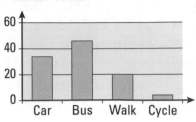

a How many students walked during the summer term?

b How many students cycled during the winter term?

c What was the modal way of getting to school during each term?

2 The stem-and-leaf diagrams show the heart rates for students before and after exercise.

Before exercise

4	3
5	4 5 5 6 7
6	0 3 3 4 4 5 9
7	2 2 3 4 5 5 5 7 8 8
8	0 0 1 1 4
9	2

After exercise

8	8
9	5 6 6 8
10	4 5 5 5 6 8 9 9
11	1 1 2 2 2 2 3 4 7
12	0 0 0 3
13	1 5
14	0

a How many students had a resting heart rate of 80 or above?

b How many had a heart rate above 80 after exercise?

c What was the modal heart rate

  i before exercise

  ii after exercise?

d What was the median heart rate

  i before exercise

  ii after exercise?

e What can you conclude from the above data?

example

This is a cube. How many:
  i edges **ii** faces **iii** vertices, does it have?

i 12 edges   **ii** 6 faces   **iii** 8 vertices

1 a How many edges does this shape have?
  b How many faces does this shape have?
  c How many vertices does this shape have?
  d Are there any parallel sides?
  e What is the name of this shape?

2 a How many edges does this shape have?
  b How many faces does this shape have?
  c How many vertices does this shape have?
  d What shape is the top and the base of the shape?
  e What is the name of this shape?

3 a How many edges does this shape have?
  b How many faces does this shape have?
  c How many vertices does this shape have?
  d What is the name of this shape?

4 a How many edges does this shape have?
  b How many faces does this shape have?
  c How many vertices does this shape have?
  d What is the name of this shape?

5 a Which three-dimensional shapes have no vertices?
  b Which three-dimensional shape has 6 identical faces?

Draw a net for this cube.

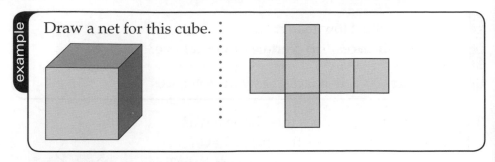

1 Draw at least four more nets for the cube above.

2 What three-dimensional shape will be made from each of these nets?

a

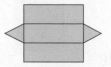

b

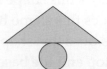

c

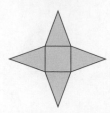

d

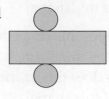

3 Draw a net for each of these shapes accurately on square paper.

a

b

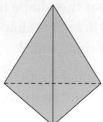

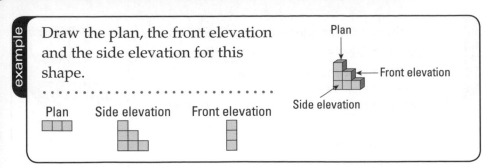

example

Draw the plan, the front elevation and the side elevation for this shape.

Plan

Front elevation

Side elevation

Plan   Side elevation   Front elevation

1 Match each of these three-dimensional shapes (**a–h**) with its front elevation (**i–viii**).

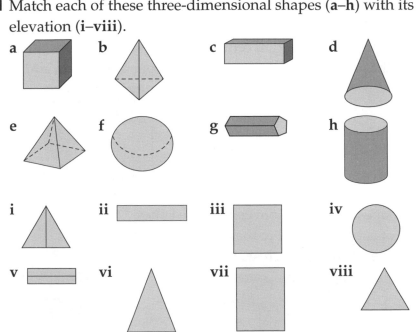

a   b   c   d

e   f   g   h

i   ii   iii   iv

v   vi   vii   viii

2 Draw the plan, the front elevation and the side elevation for each of these shapes.

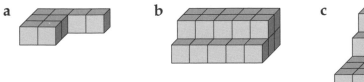

a   b   c

These shapes are made from centimetre cubes.
A layer of cubes is added to make the new shape.
What is the volume of the shape?

· ·

Bottom layer volume $= 3 \times 4 = 12$ centimetre
cubes
Middle layer volume $= 3 \times 2 = 6$ centimetre cubes
Top layer volume $\quad = 3 \times 1 = 3$ centimetre cubes
Total volume $\qquad = 12 + 6 + 3 = 21$ centimetre cubes $= 21 \, \text{cm}^3$

1 These shapes are made from centimetre cubes.
What is the volume of each shape? Given your answers in cm³.

a 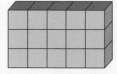   b 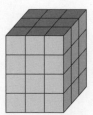   c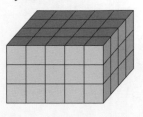

2 These shapes are made from centimetre cubes.
A layer of cubes is added to make each new shape.
What is the volume of each shape?

a    b 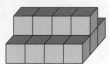   c

3 Draw three shapes that have a volume of 24 cm³.

example

Calculate the surface area of this cuboid.

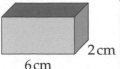

3 cm

2 cm

6 cm

This is the net of the cuboid.

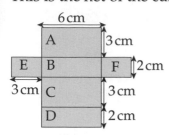

6 cm

A   3 cm

E B   F   2 cm

3 cm C   3 cm

D   2 cm

Calculate the area of each face.

Area of A and C = 3 cm × 6 cm = 18 cm²

Area of B and D = 6 cm × 2 cm = 12 cm²

Area of E and F = 3 cm × 3 cm = 6 cm²

Total surface area = 2 × 18 = 36

2 × 12 = 24

2 × 6 = 12

72 cm²

1 Draw these nets on centimetre-squared paper.

What is the area of each of these nets?

Give your answers in square centimetres (cm²).

a

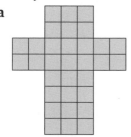

b

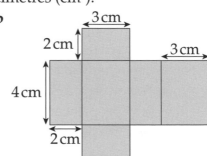

3 cm

2 cm

3 cm

4 cm

2 cm

2 Calculate the surface area of these cuboids.

a

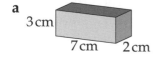

3 cm

7 cm   2 cm

b

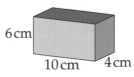

6 cm

10 cm   4 cm

c 1.5 cm

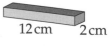

12 cm   2 cm

14a Percentage problems

a Work out 17% of £3.65
b Increase £54 by 12%.
c Decrease £45 by 16%.

a $\frac{17}{100} \times £3.65$
$= 0.17 \times £3.65$
$= £0.6205$
$= £0.62$

b $\frac{12}{100} \times £54$
$= 0.12 \times £54$
$= £6.48$
New amount
$= £54 + £6.48$
$= £60.48$

c $\frac{16}{100} \times £45$
$= 0.16 \times £45$
$= £7.20$
New amount
$= £45 + £7.20$
$= £52.20$

Choose the best method to work out these, rounding your answer appropriately.

1 a James had saved £276. He spends 86% of his savings.
How much did be spend?

b Lawson has 58 toys. He plays with 14% of his toys.
How many does he play with?

c Gabriel is learning the alphabet, which has 26 letters.
He has learnt approximately 77% of these letters.
How many letters has he learned?

d Fowey Town football stadium holds 13 560 people.
When Fowey played Polruan the stadium was 96% full.
How many people were in the stadium?

2 a Karen sells fish in her shop. Her profit last year was £132 456.
Sales have increased this year and her profit has increased by 34%.
How much profit has she made this year?

b Sanjey is on a diet. Before he started his diet he weighed 269 pounds.
He loses 27% of his weight. How much does he weigh now?

c Paul earns £540 a week. His earnings increase by 7%.
How much does he now earn?

d Ashi is training to get fit. She could run 5 miles in 54 mins. She
decreases her time by 9%. How long does it take her to run
5 miles now?

14b Proportional reasoning

Fuljan scores 45 out of 74 in her maths test and 36 out of 59 in her English test. In which test did she do better?

Maths proportion $= \frac{45}{74}$ English proportion $= \frac{36}{59}$
$= 0.6081...$ $= 0.6101...$
$= 60.81...\%$ $= 61.01...\%$
$= 60.8\%$ $= 61\%$

She did better in her English test, but only just!

1 a Glody took two tests.
He scored 37 out of 63 in his biology test. In physics he scored 48 out 95. In which test did he do better?
b Krystal put £245 in her savings account. After 1 year the interest was £15. Rosa put £147 in her savings account. After 1 year her interest was £11. Who had the better rate of interest?
c Aleem scored 12 goals in 21 games. Behzad scored 9 goals in 16 games. Who is the better goal scorer?

2 Solve each of these problems using direct proportion.
a Fourteen bananas cost £1.54. How much will five bananas cost?
b A recipe for four people uses 350 grams of rice. How much rice is needed for seven people?
c 4 kg of potatoes cost £1.29. How much will 9 kg of potatoes cost?

3 Use direct proportion to work out these.
a Four litres of Coke costs £3. Is this better value than three litres of lemonade at £2.15? Explain your answer.
b Shahnaz buys a 200-page writing pad for £1.59. Is this better value than a 135-page writing pad at £1.20? Explain your answer.
c Tammy runs 6 km in 55 minutes. Jonaid runs 4.5 km in 38 minutes. Which of them is the fastest runner?

Solve this problem using an approximation.
Anna buys 23 bars of chocolate at 29p each and 18 cans of coke at 49p each. Work out approximately how much she spent.
· ·
Chocolate: $20 \times 30 = 600p = £6$
Coke: $20 \times 50 = 1000p = £10$
She spends approximately $£6 + £10 = £16$.

1 Round each of these amounts to the given degree of accuracy.
  a £34 567 to nearest thousand   **b** £1.5687 to the nearest penny
  c 122 to nearest ten   **d** 157.89 to nearest whole number
  e 109 884 to nearest hundred   **f** 123 455 to nearest ten

2 Solve each of these problems by making an approximation.
  a Faye buys twelve ice creams at 84p each and eight bottles of water at 79p each.
     How much does she spend?
  b Satellite TV costs Claire £58.50 a month. How much does it cost per day?
  c Sonia eats 28 pieces of fruit every week. How much fruit is that in a year?
  d Ali buys nine CDs per month. How many does he buy in a year?

3 Solve each of these problems using rounding to estimate the answer. Do not use a calculator.
  a Sam has a mass of 62.5 kg.
     Her toddler has a mass of 12.1 kg.
     How many times heavier is Sam than her toddler?
  b James saves £7.75 of his pocket money each week. His dad earns £2345 a month. How many **i** weeks **ii** years, would it take for James to save the same amount as his dad earns in a month?

example

Convert these time measurements to the units indicated in the brackets.
a 1000 minutes (hours and minutes)
b 12000 days (years and days)

a $1000 \div 60 = 16.66...$ 16 hours $16\text{ hours} \times 60 = 960\text{ minutes}$
$1000 - 960 = 40\text{ minutes}$ 16 hours and 40 minutes
b $12\,000 \div 365 = 32.87...$ 32 years $32\text{ years} \times 365 = 11\,680\text{ days}$
$12\,000 - 11\,680 = 320\text{ days}$ 32 years and 320 days

1 Convert these time measurements to the units indicated in the brackets.
  a 1300 minutes (hours and minutes)
  b 3567 seconds (minutes and seconds)
  c 354 days (weeks and days)
  d 11500 days (years and days)
  e Your age in years and days (days).

2 Solve each of these problems.
  Give your answers to an appropriate degree of accuracy.
  a Twelve people win the lottery. They win £5987456 to be shared between all of them. How much does each person get?
  b 345 students and staff go on a school trip. How many 54-seater coaches do they need?
  c Sharon works on a fruit stall. She divides 238 kg of potatoes into 40 bags. What is the mass of each bag?
  d Jason spends 13945 minutes each year practicing his football skills in his garden. How many minutes is this each day?

3 Use calculator to work out these.
  Give your answers to an appropriate degree of accuracy.
  a $(3 + 4.7)^2 \div 2$ **b** $\dfrac{8.4 - 1.2^2 \times 4}{\sqrt{(2.4 + 4.1)}}$ **c** $\dfrac{32 \times (4.5 - 2.8)^2}{\sqrt{(13^2 - 4^2)}}$

Glossary

accuracy
The accuracy of data is how exact it is, for example, the number of decimal places.

add, addition
Addition is the sum of two numbers or quantities.

algebra
Algebra is the branch of mathematics where symbols or letters are used to represent numbers.

algebraic expression
An algebraic expression is a collection of numbers and letters linked by operations but not including an equals sign.

alternate angles
A pair of alternate angles are formed when a line crosses a pair of parallel lines. Alternate angles are equal.

angle: acute, obtuse, right, reflex
An angle is formed when two straight lines cross or meet each other at a point. The size of an angle is measured by the amount one line has been turned in relation to the other.

An acute angle is less than 90°.

An obtuse angle is more than 90° but less than 180°.

A right angle is a quarter of a turn, or 90°.

A reflex angle is more than 180° but less than 360°.

angle bisector
An angle bisector divides an angle in half. For example, QX is the angle bisector of ∠PQR.

angles at a point
Angles at a point add up to 360°.

$a + b + c = 360°$

angles in a quadrilateral	Angles in a quadrilateral add up to 360°.	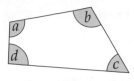 $a + b + c + d = 360°$
angles in a triangle	Angles in a triangle add up to 180°.	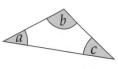 $a + b + c = 180°$
angles on a straight line	Angles on a straight line add up to 180°.	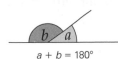 $a + b = 180°$
apex	The highest point of a solid is the apex.	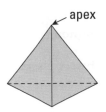
approximate, approximately	An approximate value is a value that is close to the actual value of a number.	
arc	An arc is a part of a curve.	
area: square millimetre, square centimetre, square metre, square kilometre	The area of a surface is a measure of its size.	
arithmetic sequence	In an arithmetic sequence each term is a constant amount more or less than the previous term.	
ascending, descending	Ascending means going up or getting bigger. Descending means going down or getting smaller.	
average	An average is a representative value of a set of data.	
axis, axes	An axis is one of the lines used to locate a point in a coordinate system.	

Glossary

bar chart
A bar chart is a diagram that uses rectangles of equal width to display data. The frequency is given by the height of the rectangle.

base (of plane shape or solid)
The lower horizontal edge of a plane shape is usually called the base. Similarly, the base of a solid is its lowest face.

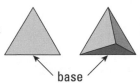

bearing, three-figure bearing
A bearing is measured from the North in a clockwise direction. The bearing of B from A is 045°.

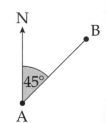

billion
One thousand million or 1 000 000 000 or 10^9.

bisect, bisector
A bisector is a line that divides an angle or another line in half.

brackets
Operations within brackets should be carried out first.

calculator: clear, display, enter, key, memory
You can use a calculator to perform calculations.

capacity: litre, millilitre centilitre
Capacity is a measure of the amount of liquid a 3-D shape will hold.

category
A category is a class of data.

centre of enlargement
The centre of enlargement is the point from which an enlargement is measured.

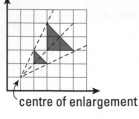

centre of enlargement

centre of rotation
The centre of rotation is the fixed point about which a rotation takes place.

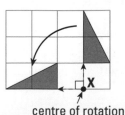

centre of rotation

change	Change is the amount of increase or decrease.
collect like terms	Collecting like terms means collecting all similar terms together. For example, $2x + 3x + 4 + 2 = 5x + 6$.
common denominator	Fractions have a common denominator if their denominators are the same.
compare	Compare means to assess the similarity of.
compasses (pair of)	Compasses are used for constructions and drawing circles.
compensation, compensate	The method of compensation makes some calculations easier, for example, some multiplications are easier if you double one of the numbers and then compensate by halving the answer.
complementary angles	Complementary angles sum to 90°. For example, $a + b = 90°$, so a and b are complementary.
conclude, conclusion	To come to a decision after a series of logical steps.
condition	A condition is something that must be satisfied.
congruent, congruence	Congruent shapes are exactly the same shape and size.
consecutive	Consecutive means following on in order. For example 2, 3 and 4 are consecutive integers.
constant	A constant is something that does not change.
construct	To draw a line, angle or shape accurately.
construction lines	Lines drawn to help in constructing bisectors of angles and lines, for example, when you use a straight edge and compasses.
continuous (data)	Continuous data can take any value between given limits, for example, less than 1 m.

Glossary

conversion graph A graph that converts between units is a conversion graph.

convert To change.

coordinate pair A coordinate pair is a pair of numbers that gives the position of a point on a coordinate grid.
For example, (3, 2) means 3 units across and 2 units up.

coordinates Coordinates are the numbers that make up a coordinate pair.

corresponding angles A pair of corresponding angles are formed when a straight line crosses a pair of parallel lines. Corresponding angles are equal.

corresponding sides Corresponding sides in congruent shapes are equal in length.

counter-example A counter-example disproves a statement.

cross-section A cross-section is what you get when you cut across a solid.

cube root The cube root of a number is the value that gives the number when multiplied by itself twice.
For example, $2 \times 2 \times 2 = 8$, so 2 is the cube root of 8, or $= \sqrt[3]{8}$.

cube, cube number A cube number is the product of three equal integers.
For example, $27 = 3 \times 3 \times 3$, so 27 is a cube number.

cubed A number is cubed if it is multiplied by itself twice.
2 cubed, written 2^3, is $2 \times 2 \times 2 = 8$.

data Data are pieces of information.

data log Data logging collects information automatically by instruments. This data can then be sent to a computer.

decimal number A decimal number is a number written using base 10 notation.

decimal place (dp)	Each column after the decimal point is called a decimal place. For example, 0.65 has two decimal places (2 dp).
deduce	To deduce is to draw a logical conclusion.
degree of accuracy	A degree of accuracy is a measure of accuracy. This can be a number of decimal places or significant figures.
denominator	The denominator is the bottom number in a fraction. It shows how many parts the whole has been divided into.
diagonal	A diagonal of a polygon is a line joining any two vertices but not forming a side.

This is a diagonal.

diagram	A diagram is a line drawing that illustrates a situation.
difference	You find the difference between two amounts by subtracting one from the other.
dimensions	The dimensions of an object are its measurements.
direct proportion	Two quantities are in direct proportion if they are always in the same ratio.
direction	The direction is the orientation of a line in space.
discrete (data)	Discrete data can only take certain definite values, for example, integers between 10 and 20.
displacement	Displacement is a measure of how something has been moved.
distance–time graph	A graph showing distance on the vertical axis and time on the horizontal axis.
distribution	Distribution describes the way data is spread out.

Glossary

divide, division	Divide (÷) means share equally.
edge (of solid)	An edge is a line along which two faces of a solid meet. 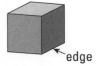
elevation	An elevation is an accurate drawing of the side or front of a solid.
enlarge, enlargement	An enlargement is a transformation that multiplies all the sides of a shape by the same scale factor.
equal (sides, angles)	Equal sides are the same length. Equal angles are the same size.
equally likely	Events are equally likely if they have the same probability.
equation	An equation is a statement linking two expressions that have the same value.
equation (of a graph)	The equation of a graph links the two variables together and can be used to give coordinates.
equidistant	Equidistant means the same distance apart.
equivalent, equivalence	Equivalent fractions are fractions with the same value.
estimate	An estimate is an approximate answer.
even	The even numbers are 2, 4, 6, 8, 10, 12, ...
event	An event is an activity or the result of an activity.
exceptional case	An exceptional case is one which is used to disprove a rule or hypothesis.
expand	To expand brackets, you multiply them out.
expect	What you expect is what you think will happen.
experiment	An experiment is a test or investigation to gather evidence for or against a theory.

experimental probability	Experimental probability is calculated on the basis of the results of an experiment.
extend	To extend a problem, you ask further questions about it.
exterior angle	An exterior angle is made by extending one side of a shape.
face	A face is a flat surface of a solid.
factor	A factor is a number that divides exactly into another number. For example, 3 and 7 are factors of 21.
fair, biased	In a fair experiment there is no bias towards any particular outcome.
flow chart	A flow chart is a diagram that describes a sequence of operations.
formula, formulae	A formula is a statement that links variables.
fraction	A fraction is a way of describing a part of a whole. For example, $\frac{2}{5}$ of the shape shown is shaded.
frequency diagram	A frequency diagram uses bars to display grouped data. The height of each bar gives the frequency of the group, and there is no space between the bars.
frequency table	A frequency table shows how often each event or quantity occurs.
function	A function is a rule. For example, +2, -3, ×4 and ÷5 are all functions.
function machine	A function machine links an input value to an output value by performing a function.
general term	The general term of a sequence is an expression which relates its value to its position in the sequence.

Glossary

generate

Generate means produce.

gradient, steepness

Gradient is the measure of the steepness of a line.

grid method

To multiply two numbers by the grid method, you work out the values in the grid, then add them.
For example, 34×17.

	30	4
10	300	40
7	210	28

$$\begin{array}{r} 300 \\ 210 \\ 40 \\ 28 \\ \hline 578 \end{array}$$

grouped data

Grouped data are groups of data values.

hectare

A hectare is a unit of area equal to 10 000 m².

height, high

Height is the vertical distance from the base to the top of a shape.

heptagon

A seven-sided shape.

highest common factor (HCF)

The highest common factor is the largest factor that is common to two or more numbers.
For example, the HCF of 12 and 8 is 4.

horizontal

A horizontal line is parallel to the bottom of the page.

hypothesis, hypotheses

A hypothesis is a statement that has not been shown to be true or untrue.

identity

An identity is an equation that is always true.

imperial unit: foot, yard, mile, pint, gallon ounce, pound, ton

Imperial units are the units of measurement historically used in the UK and other English-speaking countries.

increase, decrease

Increase means make greater. Decrease means make less.

index, indices, power

The index of a number tells you how many of the number must be multiplied together. When a number is written in index notation, the index or power is the raised number.
For example, the index of 4^2 is 2. The plural of index is indices.

input, output

Input is data fed into a machine or process. Output is the data produced by a machine or process.

integer	An integer is a positive or negative whole number (including zero). The integers are: ..., -3, -2, -1, 0, 1, 2, 3, ...
intercept	The *y*-intercept is the point where a graph crosses the *y*-axis.
interest	Interest is the amount paid by someone who borrows money. Interest is calculated as a percentage of the sum borrowed.
interior angle	An interior angle is inside a shape, between two adjacent sides.
interpret	You interpret data or a question when you make sense of it.
intersect, intersection	Two lines intersect at the point where they cross. intersection
inverse	An inverse operation has the opposite effect to the original operation. For example, multiplication is the inverse of division.
investigate	To investigate something, you find out more about it.
isometric	Isometric grids are designed to make it easier to draw shapes.
justify	To justify is to explain or to prove right.
length: millimetre, centimetre, metre, kilometre; mile, foot, inch	Length is a measure of distance. It is often used to describe one dimension of a shape.
line graph	Points are joined by straight lines on a line graph.
linear equation, linear expression, linear function, linear relationship	An equation, expression, function or relationship is linear if the highest power of any variable it contains is 1. For example, $y = 3x - 4$ is a linear equation.

Glossary

linear sequence   The terms of a linear sequence increase by the same amount each time.

locus, loci   A locus is the position of a set of points, usually a line, that satisfies some given condition. Loci is the plural of locus.

lowest common multiple (LCM)   The lowest common multiple is the smallest multiple that is common to two or more numbers.
For example, the LCM of 4 and 6 is 12.

map   A mapping maps one set of numbers to another.

mapping   A mapping is a rule that can be applied to a set of numbers to give another set of numbers.

mass: gram, kilogram, tonne; ounce, pound   Mass is a measure of the amount of matter in an object. An object's mass is closely linked to its weight.

mean   The mean is an average value found by adding all the data values and dividing by the number of pieces of data.

median   The median is an average which is the middle value when the data is arranged in size order.

metric unit: gram, metre, litre   Metric units are the measurements used in the metric system.

midpoint   The midpoint of a line is halfway between the two endpoints.

mirror line   A mirror line is a line or axis of symmetry.

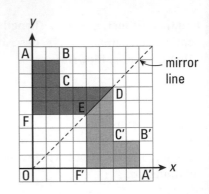

modal class   The modal class is the most commonly occurring class when the data is grouped. It is the class with the highest frequency.

mode   The mode is an average which is the data value that occurs most often.

model   A model is an experiment that attempts to copy a real-life pattern.

multiple   A multiple of an integer is the product of that integer and any other.
For example, these are multiples of 6: $6 \times 4 = 24$ and $6 \times 12 = 72$.

multiply, multiplication   Multiplication is the operation of combining two numbers or quantities to form a product.

multiply out (expressions)   A bracket is multiplied out when each term inside it is multiplied by the term outside it.
For example, $3(x + 1)$ multiplied out is $3x + 3$.

negative number   A negative number is a number less than zero.

net   A net is a 2-D arrangement that can be folded to form a solid shape.

***n*th term**   The nth term is the general term of a sequence.

numerator   The numerator is the top number in a fraction. It shows how many parts you are dealing with.

object, image   The object is the original shape before a transformation. The image is the position of the object after a transformation.

occur   To occur means to happen.

odd   The odd numbers are 1, 3, 5, 7, 9, 11, ...

order   To order means to arrange according to size or importance.

Glossary

order of operations
The conventional order of operations is:
brackets first,
then division and multiplication,
then addition and subtraction.

order of rotational symmetry
The order of rotational symmetry is the number of times that a shape will fit on to itself during a full turn.

origin
The origin is the point where the x- and y-axes cross, that is $(0, 0)$.

outcome
An outcome is the result of a trial or experiment.

parallel
Two lines that always stay the same distance apart are parallel. Parallel lines never cross or meet.

partition, part
To partition means to split a number into smaller amounts, or parts.
For example, 57 could be split into 50 + 7, or 40 + 17.

percentage (%)
A percentage is a fraction expressed as the number of parts per hundred.

perimeter
The perimeter of a shape is the distance around it. It is the total length of the edges.

perpendicular
Two lines are perpendicular to each other if they meet at a right angle.

perpendicular bisector
The perpendicular bisector of a line is at right angles to the line at its midpoint.

pie chart
A pie chart uses a circle to display data. The angle at the centre of a sector is proportional to the frequency.

place value: thousands hundreds, tens, units, tenths hundredths, thousandths
The place value is the value of a digit in a number.
For example, in 3.65 the digit 6 has a value of 6 tenths.

plan, plan view	A plan view of a solid is the view from directly overhead.
polygon: pentagon, hexagon, heptagon, octagon	A polygon is a closed shape with three or more straight edges.

A pentagon has five sides.

A hexagon has six sides.

A heptagon has seven sides.

An octagon has eight sides.

population pyramid	A population pyramid is a back-to-back bar chart (Homework) showing the differences between two populations.
predict	Predict means forecast in advance.
primary source	Data you collect yourself is data from a primary source.
prime	A prime number is a number that has exactly two different factors.
prime factor	Expressing a number as the product of its prime factors is prime decomposition factor decomposition. For example, $12 = 2 \times 2 \times 3 = 2^2 \times 3$.
probability	Probability is a measure of how likely an event is.
profit, loss	Profit is the amount of money gained. Loss is the amount of money lost.
proof, prove	A proof is a chain of reasoning that establishes the truth of a proposition.
proportion	Proportion compares the size of a part with the size of a whole. You can express a proportion as a fraction, decimal or percentage.
quadrant	A coordinate grid is divided into four quadrants by the x- and y-axes.

Glossary

quadrilateral: kite, parallelogram, rectangle, rhombus, square, trapezium

A quadrilateral is a polygon with four sides.

rectangle

All angles are right angles. Opposite sides equal.

parallelogram

Two pairs of parallel sides.

kite

Two pairs of adjacent sides equal.

rhombus

All sides the same length. Opposite angles equal.

square

All sides and angles equal.

trapezium

One pair of parallel sides.

questionnaire
A questionnaire is a list of questions used to gather information in a survey.

random
A selection is random if each object or number is equally likely to be chosen.

range
The range is the difference between the largest and smallest values in a set of data.

ratio
Ratio compares the size of one part with the size of another part.

rearrange
To rearrange a formula, you reposition the terms.

recurring decimal
A recurring decimal has an unlimited number of digits, which form a pattern, after the decimal point.

reflect, reflection
A reflection is a transformation in which corresponding points in the object and the image are the same distance from the mirror line.

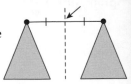

reflection symmetry
A shape has reflection symmetry if it has a line of symmetry.

regular	A regular polygon has equal sides and equal angles.
relationship	A relationship is a link between objects or numbers.
rotate, rotation	A rotation is a transformation in which every point in the object turns through the same angle relative to a fixed point.
round	You round a number by expressing it to a given degree of accuracy. For example, 639 is 600 to the nearest 100 and 640 to the nearest 10. To round to one decimal place means to round to the nearest tenth. For example, 12.47 is 12.5 to 1 dp.
sample	A sample is part of a population.
sample space (diagram)	A sample space diagram records the outcomes of two events.
scale, scale factor	A scale gives the ratio between the size of the object and its diagram. A scale factor is the multiplier in an enlargement.
scale drawing	A scale drawing of something has every part reduced or enlarged by the same amount, the scale factor.
scatter graph	A scatter graph is a graph on which pairs of observations are plotted.
secondary source	Data already collected is data from a secondary source.
sector	A sector is a division of a pie chart.
service charge	The cost for providing the service.
sign change key	The sign change key $\boxed{+/-}$ on a calculator changes a positive value to negative or vice versa.
simplest form	A fraction (or ratio) is in its simplest form when the numerator and denominator (or parts of the ratio) have no common factors. For example, $\frac{3}{5}$ is expressed in its simplest form.

Glossary

simplify

To simplify an expression you multiply out any brackets and collect like terms together.

simulation

A simulation is a mathematical model.

slope

A slope or gradient is the measure of steepness of a line.

solid (3-D) shape: cube, cuboid, prism, pyramid, square-based pyramid, tetrahedron

A solid is a shape formed in three-dimensional space.

cube

six square faces

cuboid

six rectangular faces

prism

end faces are the same shape and size

pyramid

the faces meet at a common vertex

tetrahedron

all the faces are triangles

square-based pyramid

the base is a square

solve (an equation)

To solve an equation you need to find the value of the variable that will make the equation true.

square number, squared

If you multiply a number by itself the result is a square number.
For example, 25 is a square number because
$5^2 = 5 \times 5 = 25$.

square root

A square root is a number that when multiplied by itself is equal to a given number.
For example, $\overline{25} = 5$, because $5 \times 5 = 25$.

statistic, statistics

A statistic is a value that represents a set of data.
A mean, median, mode and range are statistics.

stem-and-leaf diagram   A stem-and-leaf diagram is a way of displaying data.
For example, the numbers 29, 16, 18, 8, 4, 16, 27, 19, 13 and
15 could be displayed as:

0	4 8
1	3 5 6 6 8 9
2	7 9

Key: 0 │ 4   means 4

straight edge   A ruler.

straight-line graph   When coordinate
points lie in
a straight line
they form a
straight-line
graph. It is the
graph of a linear
equation.

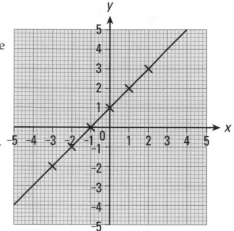

strategy   A strategy is a way of tackling a problem.

substitute   When you substitute you replace part of an expression
with a numerical value.

subtract, subtraction   Subtraction is the operation that finds the difference in
size between two numbers.

supplementary angles   Supplementary angles add up to 180°.
For example, 60° and 120° are supplementary angles.

surface, surface area   The surface area of a solid is the total area of its faces.

systematic   To work systematically means to break a problem down
into simple steps, which you can solve individually.
To list data systematically, you could divide the data
into groups and list items for one group at a time

Glossary

T(*n*)

T(*n*) is the notation for the general, *n*th, term of a sequence.
For example, T(3) is the third term.

tax

Taxes are paid to the government. They are often expressed as a percentage.

term

A term is a number or object in a sequence. It is also part of an expression.

terminating decimal

A terminating decimal has a limited number of digits after the decimal point.

tessellate, tessellation

A tessellation is a tiling pattern with no gaps. Shapes will tessellate if they can be put together to make such a pattern.

theoretical probability

A theoretical probability is worked out without an experiment.

theory

A theory is a collection of ideas explaining something.

three-dimensional (3-D)

Any solid shape is three-dimensional.

to the power of *n*

This is the index in a number expressed in index notation in general form, for example x^n.

total

The total is the result of an addition.

transform

You transform an equation by doing the same to both sides.

transformation

A transformation moves a shape from one place to another.

translate, translation

A translation is a transformation in which every point in an object moves the same distance and direction. It is a sliding movement.

tree diagram	A tree diagram shows the probabilities of the outcomes of an event. For example, if you roll a dice:	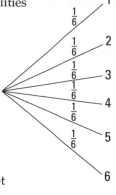

trial	In probability, a trial is one attempt in an experiment.

triangle: equilateral, isosceles, scalene, right-angled

A triangle is a polygon with three sides.

equilateral   isosceles   scalene   right-angled

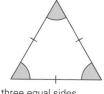 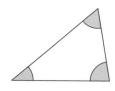 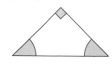

three equal sides   two equal sides   no equal sides   one angle is 90°

triangular prism	A triangular prism has a triangular cross-section all the way through.	

two-way table

A two-way table shows the outcomes of two independent events.
For example, the result when you roll two dice and add the scores.

		Dice 1					
		1	2	3	4	5	6
Dice 2	1	2	3	4	5	6	7
	2	3	4	5	6	7	8
	3	4	5	6	7	8	9
	4	5	6	7	8	9	10
	5	6	7	8	9	10	11
	6	7	8	9	10	11	12

Glossary

unit fraction

A unit fraction has 1 as the numerator.
For example, $\frac{1}{2}$, $\frac{1}{7}$, $\frac{1}{23}$.

unitary method

In the unitary method, you first work out the size of a single unit and then scale it up or down.

value added tax (VAT)

A tax imposed on goods and services by the government.

variable

A variable is a symbol that can take a range of values.

vary

Results vary if they are different each time.

verify

To verify something is to show it is true.

vertex, vertices

A vertex of a 3-D shape is a point at which three or more edges meet.
A vertex of a 2-D shape is where two sides meet.

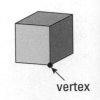

vertex

vertical

A vertical line is parallel to the side of the page.

volume: cubic millimetre, cubic centimetre, cubic metre

The volume of an object is a measure of how much space it occupies.

x-axis, y-axis

On a coordinate grid, the x-axis is the horizontal axis and the y-axis is the vertical axis.

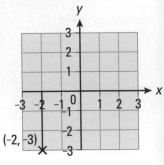